The Animal Kingdom

An Introduction to the Major Groups of Animals

by George S. Fichter

Illustrations by Charles Harper

GOLDEN PRESS NEW YORK

Foreword

So important are the satisfaction and development of the interest in animal life that is the heritage of young people everywhere, that no possible means for furthering it can be overlooked. Even a general knowledge of the more than a million kinds of animals that share the world with us is bound to provide a broadening of interests and horizons that will endure throughout adult life. More than that, it can help arouse sympathy and aid for the wild life and wild places so rapidly disappearing from the earth.

In *The Animal Kingdom,* George S. Fichter has provided a remarkably useful source of animal information that ranges from the simple one-celled protozoans to man himself. To do this, he has concentrated an immense amount of material in plain, readily understandable terms but with no "writing down"—a feat too seldom accomplished. Even the plentiful descriptions of animals are full of interest and always enlivened by accounts of relationships, ways of life and means for securing food. All with that almost complete avoidance of technical terms that is a special feature of this book.

A word must be said on the unconventional illustrations by Charles Harper. At first glance, these may seem to be merely fanciful, but a second look reveals that they are not simply attractive pictures but actually emphasize the basic essentials of line, form and color. Their faint touch of humor by no means detracts—indeed, makes learning so much easier. Concise and well-considered captions assure understanding of the action depicted. As a confirmed and much-abused realist in matters of animal art, I have been won over completely by Mr. Harper's clever and interesting interpretations.

Lee S. Crandall
General Curator Emeritus
New York Zoological Park

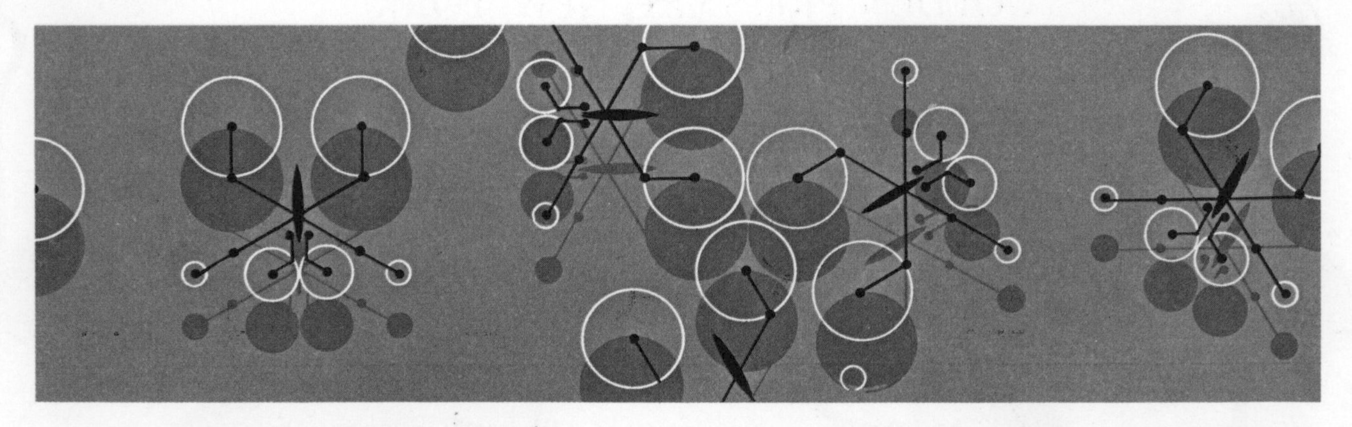

 Produced in the U.S.A. by Western Publishing Company, Inc. Published by Golden Press, New York, N.Y. Library of Congress Catalog Card Number: 68-26811

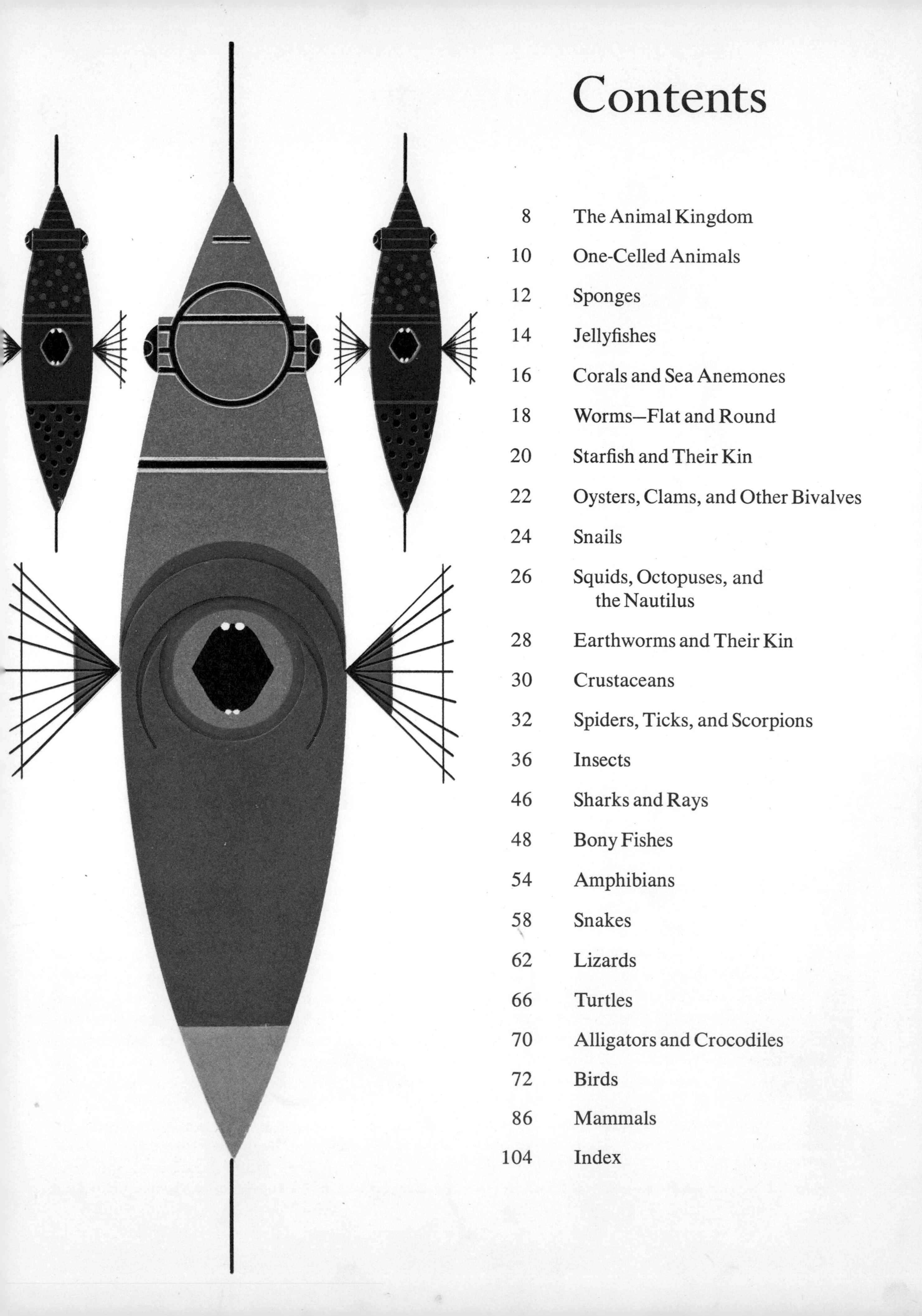

Contents

These prairie dogs have what all animals seek—food, a place to live, and an opportunity to produce more of their kind.

The Animal Kingdom

More than a million kinds of animals inhabit the earth. They are found from the dark depths of the sea to the tops of mountains and from frigid pole to frigid pole. All have the same basic needs. One of the most important is food, which provides the substances an animal uses in building and repairing its body. It furnishes the energy needed to keep the animal going—which is usually to find more food.

Many animals live a solitary life. Except at mating time or, in some cases, while rearing their young, these animals live entirely independent of others of their own kind. Still other animals exist in colonies or in groups. Some of the one-celled animals, the corals, and the sponges may be connected physically to other individuals in associations known as colonies. Such insects as bees, ants, and termites are organized into social groups in which there is division of labor to assure success of the group.

Schools of fish, herds of grazing animals, packs of wolves or of other predators, flocks of birds—these are groups of animals that travel together and are bonded by similar feeding habits and behavior. Most unusual of the animal associations are those in which the animals are different. In some cases one of the animals benefits, but the other is not harmed. Remoras attach themselves by the sucker on their head to a shark, turtle, or other sea creature. They feed on scraps of food left over from their host's meal, and the host neither gains nor loses from the association. The

In parasitism, the eel-like lamprey preys on a lake trout (upper left).

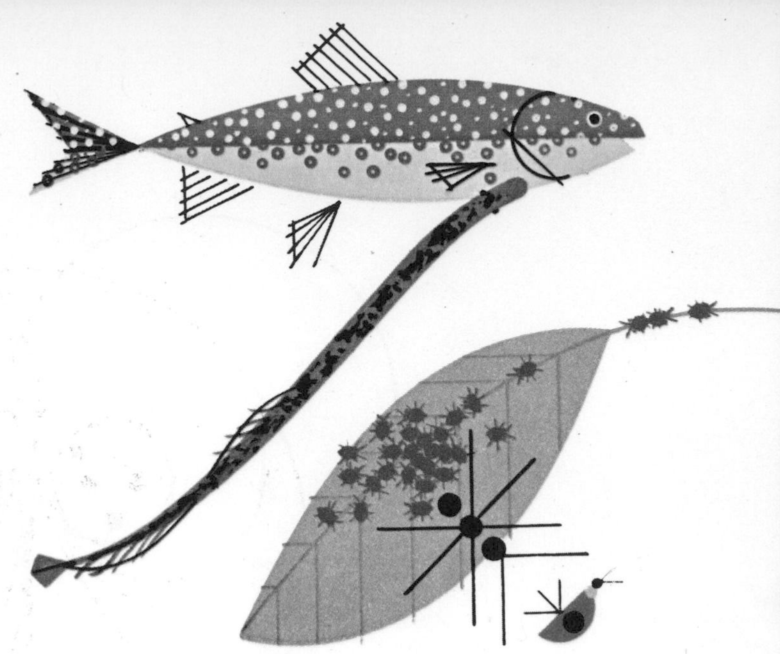

In a symbiotic relationship, ants protect aphids from predatory ladybug and later reward themselves with honeydew secreted by the aphids.

remora can release itself and pick another ride whenever it chooses. Cattle egrets follow herds of cattle or other grazing animals to feed on insects stirred up by the larger animals.

In another type of association, called symbiosis, both animals benefit from the association. Termites, for example, contain in their digestive tract some one-celled animals that are unable to live in any other kind of habitat. But in turn, the termites depend on the one-celled animals to digest the cellulose in wood for them. The termites cannot live if the one-celled animals are removed. Sea anemones ordinarily are attached to stationary objects but may fasten themselves to shells occupied by hermit crabs. In this way they are carried to new places to find food. The hermit crab probably gains from being partially hidden by the anemone and protected from attackers by the poisonous stingers in its tentacles.

Most one-sided of all the animal associations is that of the parasite and its host. Only the parasite benefits, but if the host eventually dies from the effects of the parasite, the parasite wins a bitter victory.

The strongest competitor of any animal is a member of its own species, for they share the same basic needs. The fight with members of the same species for food and living space is constant, and only the strong survive in these competitions. The various societies of man, for example, contain all the types of associations, but man's greatest conflicts are with other men.

Scientists divide animals into large groups, called phyla, on the basis of similarity and relationship. The most important of these groups are surveyed in the chapters in this book.

All these red-winged blackbirds are competing for the same morsel—a juicy caterpillar.

This weird one-celled creature is a parasitic flagellate that lives in man's intestines.

One-Celled Animals

Three hundred years ago, in Holland, Antony van Leeuwenhoek discovered a new world of living things. With his simple microscope, Leeuwenhoek was examining a drop of water from his rain barrel, and to his astonishment, he found it swarming with "wee animals," too small to be seen with the naked eye. These tiny creatures were given the name protozoa, which means "first animals." More than 35,000 kinds have been named.

Some one-celled animals, or protozoans, are so small that 75,000 placed end to end measure only an inch in length. A quart of water may contain as many as 50 million. They give the water color and cause it to swirl, yet they can be seen individually only with a high-powered microscope. But there are giants among the little animals, too. One species is over half an inch long. It is larger than some of the tiny crustaceans on which it preys regularly.

All one-celled animals can survive only in moist surroundings. Some live near the surface of the sea, others near the bottom. They are abundant also in fresh water, especially in stagnant or slow-moving waters, and in springs where the temperature of the water is as high as 130 degrees Fahrenheit. They abound in damp soil, and many kinds live inside the cells and tissues of plants or larger animals. When their environment becomes dry, some species form a thick protective wall around their cell. They may wait for moisture to return or may be blown by the wind, like the spores of mushrooms, until finally they come to rest in moist surroundings and can resume living again.

The shapeless amoeba flows around a food particle and later moves away from the portions that are not digestible. Its "legs" are simply extensions of its cell. One to many of these "false feet" (pseudopodia) move ahead of the main part of the cell, which then flows after them. Some members of the amoeba group secrete limy shells or cement together tiny particles of sand to form a protective covering. Nearly 50 million square miles of the ocean bottom are covered with an "ooze" made up largely of these shells. The stones used to build the great pyramids of Egypt are formed of the shells of one-celled animals.

Members of another group of one-celled animals swim by a waving whiplike extension, called a flagellum. Euglena's flagellum is at the front of its cell; in other species it is at the rear. Others have two or more flagella. Euglena and other members of this group contain greenish bodies inside their cell. The green is due to chlorophyll, and so these tiny animals can manufacture their own food. Some scientists classify them as plants.

Volvox lives in colonies of many greenish cells in a globe of gelatin that rolls through the water. At night, noctiluca, a related marine protozoan, makes the sea glow bluish-green in the wake of a ship. Other protozoans of this type turn snow red or give rain puddles a bloody hue.

Among the "wee animals" that especially fascinated Leeuwenhoek were those with "incredibly thin little feet . . . which were moved very nimbly." Paramecium, common in pond waters, is the most familiar one-celled animal of this type. Its "little feet," called cilia, cover its cell like a fringe of hair. By waving these cilia, the animal rotates and spirals but nevertheless travels in a direct path, either forward or backward.

Despite their small size, one-celled animals are extremely important. Along with equally small plants, they are a basic food of countless animals. They are the beginning—the first animals—in the complex web of life.

Snow is turned red by accumulations of many millions of one-celled animals.

Drama in a drop of water—an amoeba devours a paramecium.

A red sponge beached by a tropical storm is promptly abandoned by its many tenants.

Sponges

A living bath sponge looks like a piece of gray or yellowish liver. At the market you buy only the sponge's soft skeleton after its fleshy parts have been cleaned away.

Most of the more than 5,000 species of sponges do not have soft skeletons. In their body walls are stiff spines, or spicules, that are composed either of lime or of silica (the substance of which sand is made). Those with skeletons of silica are called glass sponges, and in some kinds—Venus'-flower-basket, for example—the spines are linked together forming an intricate network. These sponges live only in deep water, some of them at depths of two miles or more. Nearly all sponges are marine, but one small group of sponges lives in fresh water.

All sponges grow attached to underwater objects. They are unable to move and are so unlike animals that, until about a century ago, they were classified as plants. It is still debated whether a sponge is one animal consisting of many cells or many one-celled animals that live together in a colony.

A simple sponge's body consists of a hollow cavity with a large opening at the end opposite where the animal is attached and many pores through the body wall. Long-necked cells that line the inside of the cavity wave whiplike flagella continually, causing a current of water to move into the pores and out the opening at the top. The sponge's cells absorb food from the water. Most sponges are not this simple, however, for their body wall contains many folds and pockets in which the food-laden water eddies.

The hollow cavities in sponges become the dwelling places for many kinds of sea creatures. A large sponge may harbor hundreds of worms, crabs, mollusks, fishes, and starfish. In the countless folds of the sponge's body they are protected from predators, which also may be turned away by the repelling odor of the living sponge. Most conveniently, as in a plush hotel, their meals are served to them in their rooms by the constant flow of water through the sponge's body cavities.

Sponges sometimes grow on the backs of crabs or on the shells occupied by hermit crabs. The benefit is mutual, for the crab is hidden from enemies and the sponge is regularly carried to new supplies of food.

Sponges reproduce either by budding—that is, new individuals appear first as tiny growths on the parent and then drop off to grow independently as new sponges—or by producing larvae that swim freely in the sea for awhile before settling down to grow and become adult sponges. In sponges the ability to replace lost parts is remarkable. If a sponge is squeezed through a sieve, some of the pieces will come together on the other side and grow into new sponges. A torn-apart sponge may thus become many sponges.

Some species of sponges form thin crusts over the object to which they are attached. Others are slim and branched, looking like underwater trees or shrubs. Some are thick-bodied, measuring five or six feet across; others are slim, delicate, and vaselike. The colors of sponges range through the spectrum—red, orange, yellow, blue, or black. Though some occur at great depths and also in cold, northern waters, sponges are most numerous and most varied in warm, shallow, tropical seas.

Since ancient times, sponges have been used for bathing and for cleaning. Synthetic sponges have largely replaced natural sponges, but sponge fishing is still an active industry in the Mediterranean, the Caribbean, and along Florida's shores. Sponges are even planted in underwater farms, but they grow slowly.

Sponges are harvested by divers or with nets (trawls) that are dragged along the bottom to scrape them up. In the boat, the sponges are killed, generally by trampling them, and then are hung on ropes in the sun so that the soft parts will decay and slough away. Finally, they are sorted and trimmed for market.

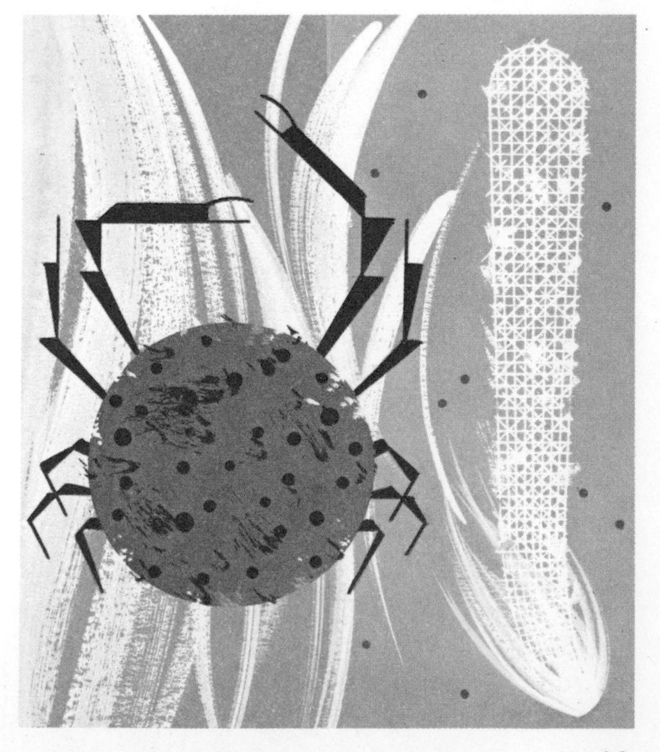

A bath sponge serves as camouflage for a spider crab (to left). The complex skeleton of a Venus'-flower-basket sponge (right).

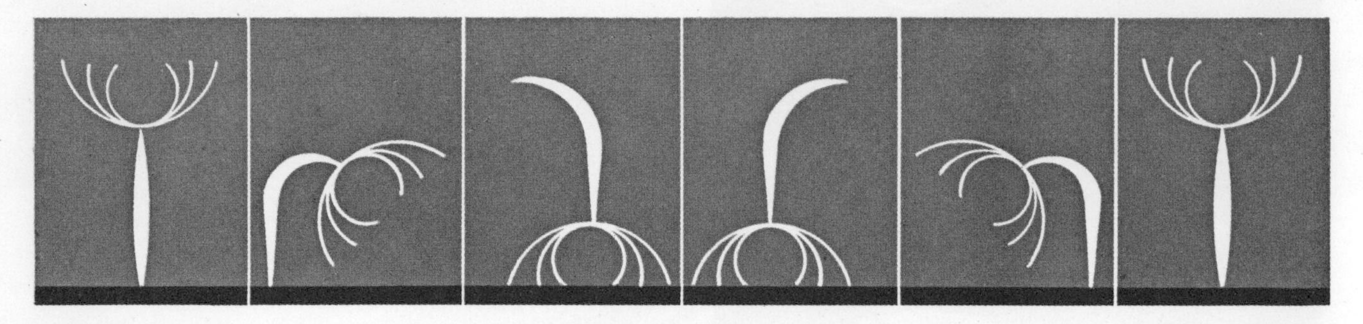

A hydra travels by turning cartwheels.

Jellyfishes

The pink jellyfish that lives in the cold waters of both the Atlantic and Pacific oceans measures as much as seven feet across its bell-shaped body. Its tentacles may be 50 feet long. This giant jellyfish is the largest of the some 10,000 species in its group. Almost all of them live in salt water. All have a central body with only one opening to the outside.

Hydra, the common animal studied in laboratories, lives in fresh water. A tiny creature less than half an inch long, it is often abundant in ponds, lakes, and streams. Hydra has a simple, tubelike body. Usually, it clings to objects by its base, or foot, but sometimes it drifts head down by means of a balloon-like float secreted from its base. Six to a dozen tentacles surround its mouth, waving constantly and grabbing any food they contact. A network of nerve fibers stimulates the animal to move away from conditions that make it uncomfortable and toward those that are favorable. It moves by sliding along on its foot or by looping end over end.

Like its relatives, hydra has special cells in its tentacles that aid in overcoming prey. These are triggered when touched or when stimulated by chemical changes in the water near them. Some of the cells release barbed spears and a powerful poison that is deadly to small animals. Other cells are sticky lashes in which the prey becomes tangled.

Most of hydra's close relatives live in salt water. Obelia is a common type that grows in a moss-like colony with branches up to six inches long. Dense growths are often seen on pilings. The colony's central stalk is fastened, or rooted, to a rock, piling, or other object on which the colony is growing.

Obelia produces buds that develop into small animals resembling jellyfish. These are released and swim freely, eventually producing eggs and sperm that unite. Fertilized eggs grow into new colonies. In the group to which the true jellyfishes belong, the bell-shaped body is the large, dominant stage. The attached stage, when the

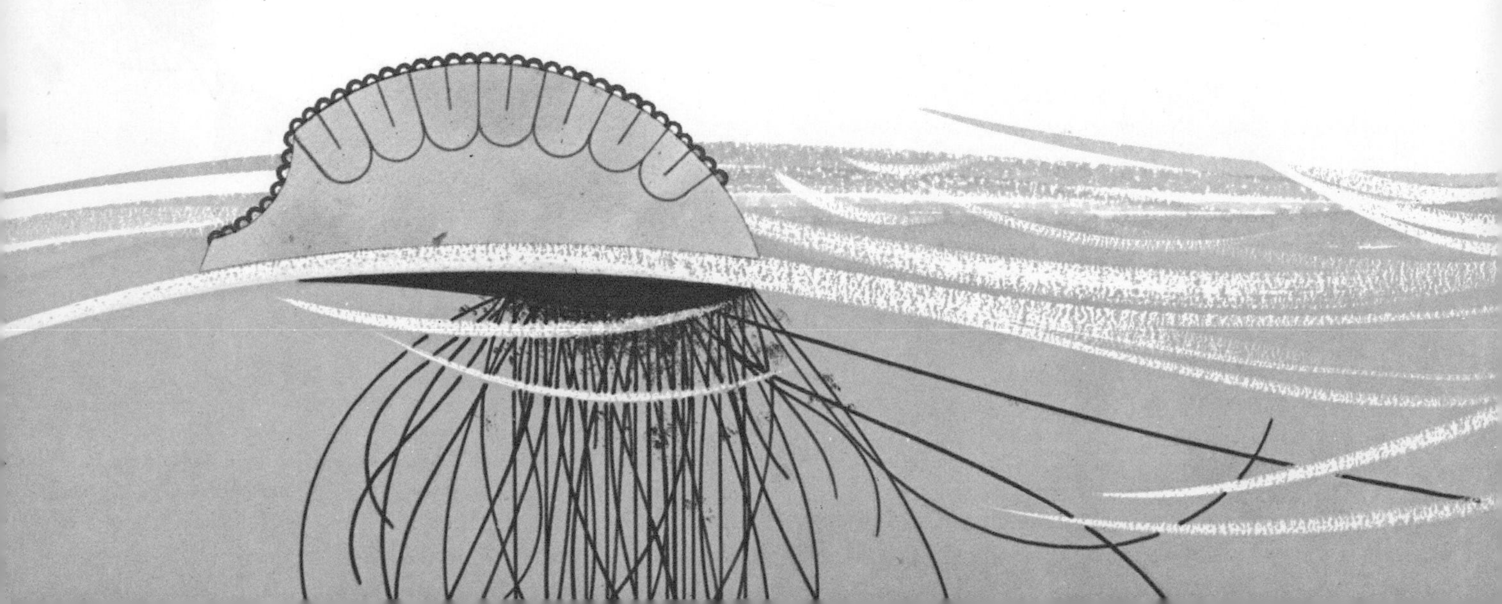

Glistening moon jellies ride the waves.

body is tubular like a hydra's, is either small or does not occur at all.

The Portuguese man-o'-war, found in warm seas and in the Atlantic along the coast of North America, is one of the most unusual members of the group. It is actually a floating colony of animals that sails the sea by means of a large gas-filled bubble. The colorful float rides above the surface of the water so that the colony is swept along by the wind and waves. The Portuguese man-o'-war's tentacles, which may be 50 feet long, have stinging cells that can kill fish or other small animals. The stings are very painful to swimmers. Beaches are vacated when large numbers of these curious creatures appear.

The purple sail is a jellyfish that rides the seas with a gas-filled float. This animal can adjust the amount of gas in its float, lifting it high when the winds are right for sailing and keeping it low in stormy weather.

Another member of this same group is the fire coral, or stinging coral. It grows in dense, branching tufts, commonly covered with a heavy limy coat, and it does, in fact, aid in building reefs. But like its relatives, the fire coral animal has stinging cells on its tentacles, and the stings are extremely painful.

True jellyfish are sometimes seen in large schools, either floating quietly on the surface or pumping their bells so that they swim with an up-and-down motion through the water. Tentacles hang down around the rim of the jellyfish's bell and, in most jellyfish, the tentacles contain stinging cells. Some of the smaller jellyfish sting so severely that they are called sea wasps. Many fish use the umbrella-like bell of a jellyfish as a place of refuge to hide from enemies, but they must be wary themselves so that they are not caught.

The upside-down jellyfish differs from other jellyfish in having no stinging cell in its tentacles. The central stalk under the umbrella, containing the mouth and digestive tract, is very large and is divided into numerous lobes. Inside these lobes are tiny plants, or algae. As the jellyfish floats or swims in the shallows in its upside-down position, it spreads these lobes so that the algae get the full benefit of the sun. The tiny plants then manufacture food, and some algae in turn become food for the jellyfish.

A Portuguese man-o'-war captures a snapper with its stinging tentacles. At the same time a hawksbill turtle eats the Portuguese man-o'-war, closing its eyes to avoid the stings.

Corals and Sea Anemones

Coral reefs were one of the great hazards to sailing vessels exploring tropical seas in early days. Many ships were wrecked on the stony reefs in storms. Great Barrier Reef, the largest of the many reefs that occur in warm, shallow seas around the world, stretches for more than 1,200 miles along the eastern coast of Australia. In some places it is nearly 100 miles wide. Between the reef and the continent is a broad, shallow channel, 20 to 30 miles wide, dotted with islands. On the sea side, the reef is exposed to the great power of the waves of the open Pacific. They pound against the rock wall relentlessly and with thundering booms. On the Pacific side the reef drops off sharply into water thousands of feet deep.

Thousands of islands in the South Pacific are formed mainly of masses of coral that have been exposed above the sea long enough for plants to grow on them. The most interesting of these are called atolls, which are coral islands in a solid or broken ring around a shallow, central lagoon. Scientists believe that atolls were formed when reefs that fringed an island continued to build up while the island itself sank into the sea. The coral islands are seldom more than 20 feet above sea level.

Many islands of the Florida Keys are the remains of ancient coral reefs. Just off Key Largo, the northernmost island in the chain, is an underwater park where a coral reef and its many inhabitants are preserved for the public to enjoy.

Coral animals belong to the same group of animals as hydras, jellyfish, and their relatives. Some thrive in cold seas, as far north as Norway and Newfoundland, but reef-forming corals will not grow in water deeper than 150 feet or colder than 68 degrees Fahrenheit. Coral animals have a soft, jelly-like body, but those that form reefs secrete a protective, cup-shaped limy skeleton around themselves. A coral reef is formed of many millions of these skeletons. As older animals die, leaving their skeletons, new ones grow on top, building the reef upward. The animals also grow at the sides, spreading the reef over a greater area. Most of the large reefs in existence today have been in the process of formation for at least 10,000 years. The reefs are strengthened by lime secreted by algae that grow over the coral.

Skin divers find coral reefs an exciting underwater world to explore. The many species of coral occur in a great variety of sizes, shapes, and colors. During the day the coral animals stay hidden in their stony cups. At night they extend their tentacles to feed so that the coral reef literally blooms. And the reefs are inhabited by beautiful and bizarre tropical fishes, shellfish, and crustaceans. The reef is filled with caves and crannies in which creatures can hide. Unlike hydras and jellyfishes, the corals do not possess stinging cells in their tentacles. Coral cuts are slow to heal, however, apparently due to a poison from the coral animals.

Not all coral animals are stony. These include sea whips, dead man's fingers, and other corals that have a soft, leathery skeleton. They bend and sway in the currents over the reefs.

Sea anemones, closely related to corals, are also protected by a tough skin rather than by a hard skeleton. They are usually fastened to the bottom or to shells or other objects, but they can glide slowly from place to place on their foot or base. When feeding, a sea anemone spreads its tentacles wide and waves them to catch food. When disturbed, the anemone draws in its tentacles and closes its mouth. Anemones do have stinging cells in their tentacles.

Many sea anemones have such colorful and delicate tentacles that the animals look like flowers. The name of the group to which they belong is Anthozoa, which means "flower animal." Most sea anemones are only about three or four inches tall, but an anemone that lives in the warm waters of Australia's Great Barrier Reef is more than 12 inches tall and twice as broad. Small fish use its body cavity as a hiding place.

A few of the many kinds of colorful fish and coral animals that make up a coral reef community.

Worms—Flat and Round

Most long, legless creatures are called worms. Caterpillars of butterflies and moths, legless lizards, fly maggots, and burrowing snakes are among the many kinds of wormlike animals. But to biologists, worms are particular kinds of animals. The two largest phyla are the flatworms, about 9,000 species, and the roundworms, about 3,000 species. Segmented worms, or annelids, of which the most familiar member is the earthworm, form a third group (see page 28).

Worm parasites are responsible for many diseases of man and his animals. Trichinosis is caused by roundworms that form hard cysts in the muscles of hogs and then are released when the muscle, or meat, is eaten. Thorough cooking kills the worms. Elephantiasis is a tropical disease in which legs or arms swell to immense size as the flow of lymph is blocked by a kind of roundworm. The worms are transmitted through the bites of mosquitoes. Hookworms, intestinal roundworms, and pinworms are other common roundworm parasites.

The most familiar flatworm parasite is the tapeworm. A tapeworm may grow to a length of more than 40 feet. Its tiny head, about one twenty-fifth of an inch long, is attached by strong

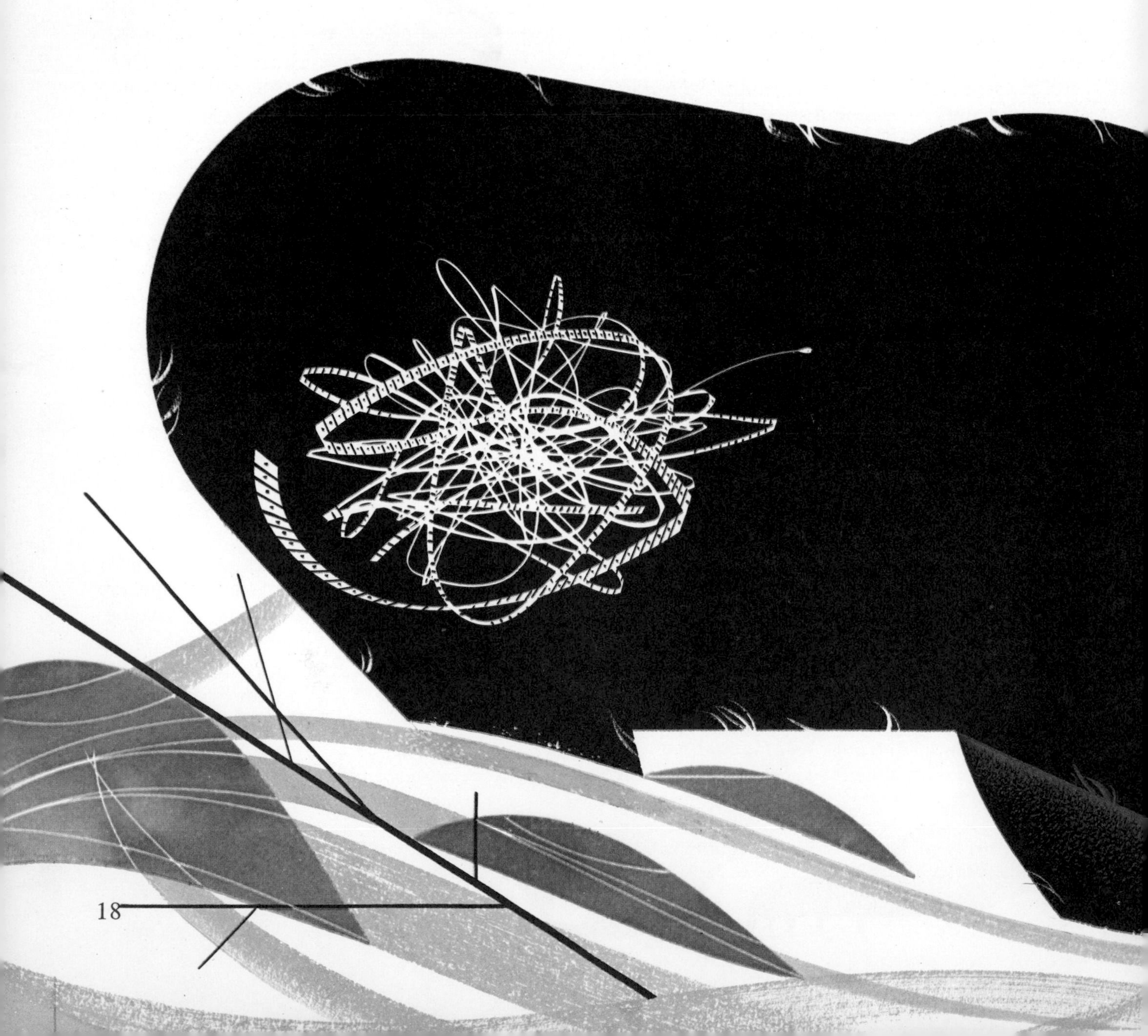

hooks to the host's intestinal wall. Each body segment behind the head is slightly larger than the one before, and each absorbs its food directly through its body wall. There may be as many as 3,000 segments. Eventually the end segment becomes "ripe," breaks loose and passes from the host's body in wastes. Inside are thousands of eggs that hatch and live in the soil until picked up in the food of another animal.

Many worm parasites spend part of their life in one animal and part in another. A liver fluke's eggs pass out of the host animal's body in its wastes and hatch into tiny larvae that swim through water. They infest only one kind of snail. After a time the larvae leave the snail and form a resting stage on a blade of grass. If they are then eaten by sheep, they become adult worms in the host's liver. Obviously, there are so many chances of failure in such a life cycle that it is a wonder any worms ever survive. Each worm produces a great many eggs, as many as half a million, and every egg that finds the right kind of snail host divides a number of times so that several hundred adult worms may result from one egg.

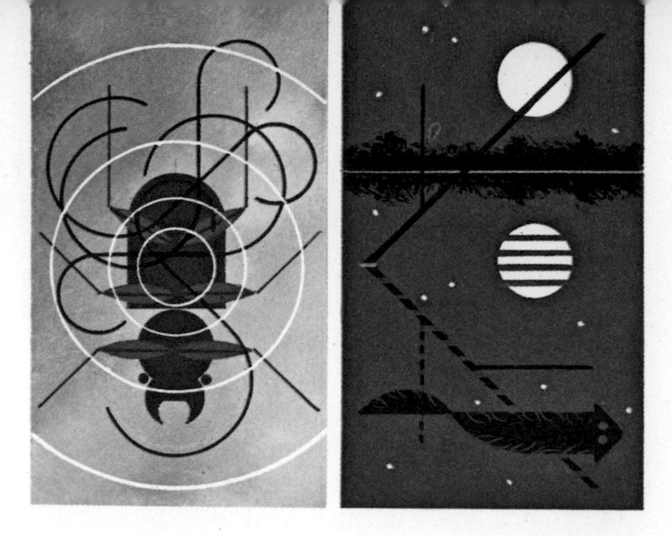

These horsehair worms escaping from the dead body of a stag beetle will mature in a rain puddle (left).

Planaria, a flatworm, comes to the surface at night to feed (right).

Worms also infest plants. Nematodes live in the soil where they feed on the roots and underground portions of stems. They have a sharp beak with which they pierce roots or stems and then suck out the juices. Plants are deformed, weakened, and eventually killed. An acre of rich soil may contain as many as three billion nematodes. They are among the most common of all animals, yet few people know they exist.

Planarians are free-living flatworms found under rocks, sticks or other debris in streams or ponds. They have a soft, flat body about half an inch long, and though they can swim, they usually crawl or glide along in a track made of their own slime. Planarians feed on small animals, either living or dead. If a planarian is cut into pieces, each piece grows into a new worm.

Wriggling knots of horsehair worms, closely related to roundworms, appear in rain puddles or in ponds. Once it was believed that they were horsehairs that had come to life. Female horsehair worms lay strings of eggs up to seven and a half feet long, and the larvae burrow into the bodies of immature insects in which they develop.

The black bear gets fish tapeworms from eating trout and other fish. A larger tapeworm, with small, knobbed head and broader tail end, already lives in the bear's intestine. A worm may be 50 feet long, with as many thousands of segments.

Starfish and Their Kin

Sometimes starfish swarm into an oyster bed so thickly that their arms overlap. Each starfish is capable of eating an oyster or two every day.

A hungry starfish wraps its arms around an oyster's shell, and then, using the suction of the numerous tubefeet on the underside of its arms, it pulls and pulls on the oyster's closed shell. The oyster holds its shell shut as long as it can, but the starfish is persistent. Finally the muscle holding the oyster's shell shut can stand the strain no longer, and the shell pops open—not wide, perhaps, but even a slight crack is enough. Immediately the starfish sticks its stomach out through its mouth and into the oyster's shell. The starfish then digests its hard-won meal on the half-shell.

Starfish, along with sand dollars, sea urchins, sea lilies, and sea cucumbers, form a group of "spiny skinned" animals. All of the 5,000 or so species are marine. Though they are most abundant along the seashore, some kinds live in the dark depths of the sea, more than two miles beneath the surface. With exception of sea cucumbers, all have a central body disc with arms or other structures radiating from the center like the spokes of a wheel. They move by means of tubefeet that line a groove in the arms or form a spoke from the central disc. Each foot ends in a suction cup controlled by a bulb that pumps water out of the foot to create a suction. When water is pumped in again, the foot releases its hold. Nearly all members of the starfish group have spines or hard plates embedded in their skin.

Some starfish have as few as five arms, like the points on a star, but basketstars have 50 or more arms, each divided several times more toward the tip. In some species of starfish the arms are thick and short; in others, they are slim and jointed. Some starfish are bright red, purple, or yellow, and one measures almost three feet across its arms.

Starfish can grow a new arm if one is lost. In some starfish this power to replace lost parts is so astonishing that a lost arm can grow a new body. Before this was understood, oystermen who caught starfish invading their oyster beds by dragging huge rope "mops" through the beds and letting the grabby starfish entangle themselves, then cut the culprits into pieces and threw them back into the water. And they wondered why there seemed to be more and more starfish!

Sand dollars and sea urchins do not have free arms, but their disc-shaped or globular body has internal spokelike divisions. Their tubefeet are in

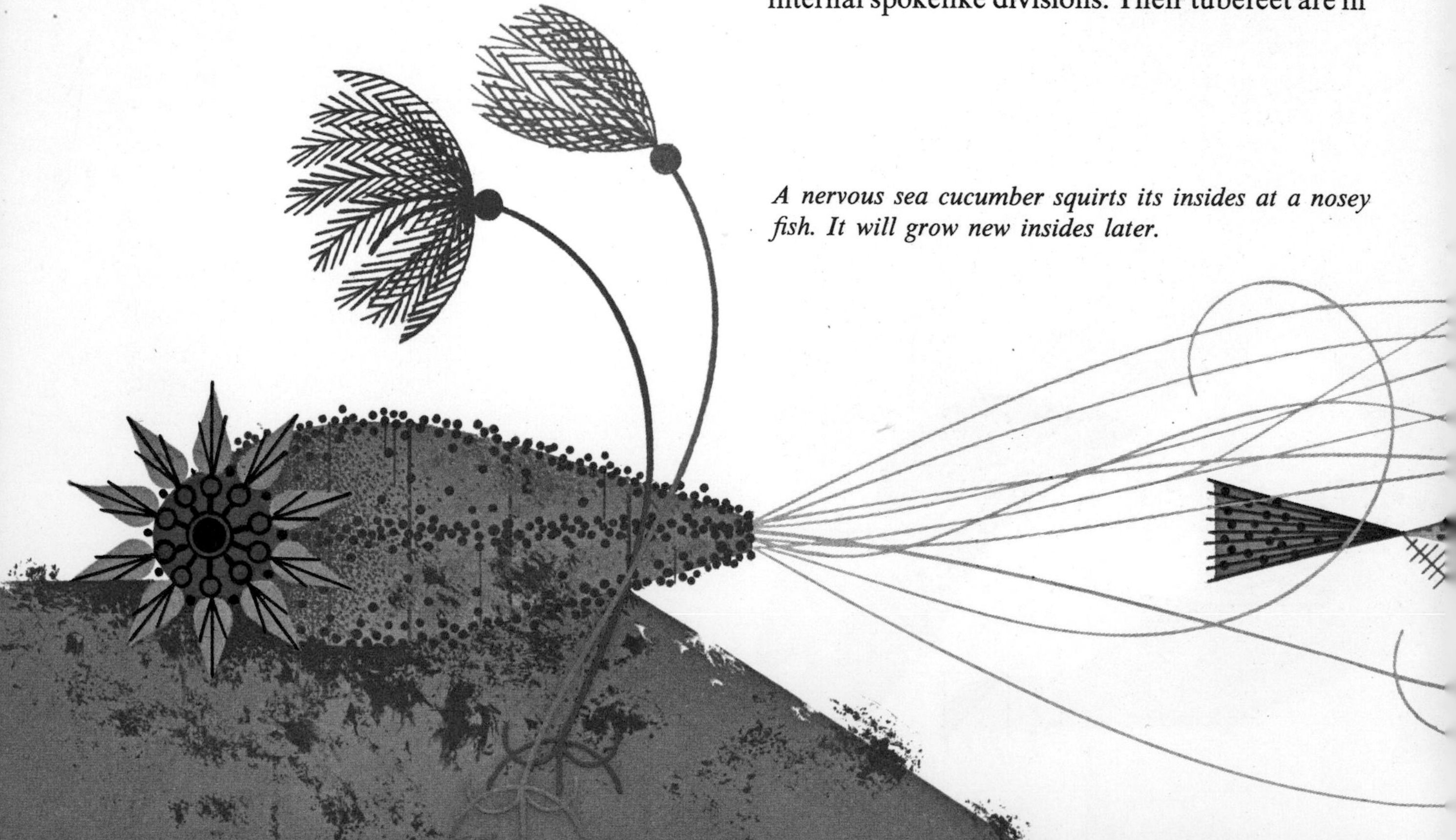

A nervous sea cucumber squirts its insides at a nosey fish. It will grow new insides later.

A sand dollar is first on a sea otter's menu. Next comes a starfish, then a sea urchin.

grooves that correspond in position to a starfish's arms. The spines surrounding their body are movable, and in some species the spines are as sharp as needles and poisonous. The six-inch spines of a sea urchin of the South Pacific are used as pencils for writing on slate. In some Asiatic countries, sea urchin eggs are eaten, either raw or cooked.

Sea lilies and feather stars grow on stalks at the top of which are many-branched, feathery arms. These colorful flower-like creatures give coral reefs the appearance of underwater gardens. Sea lilies that live in the bottom oozes in the deep sea have very long stalks. If their stalk breaks off, they can swim by waving their arms.

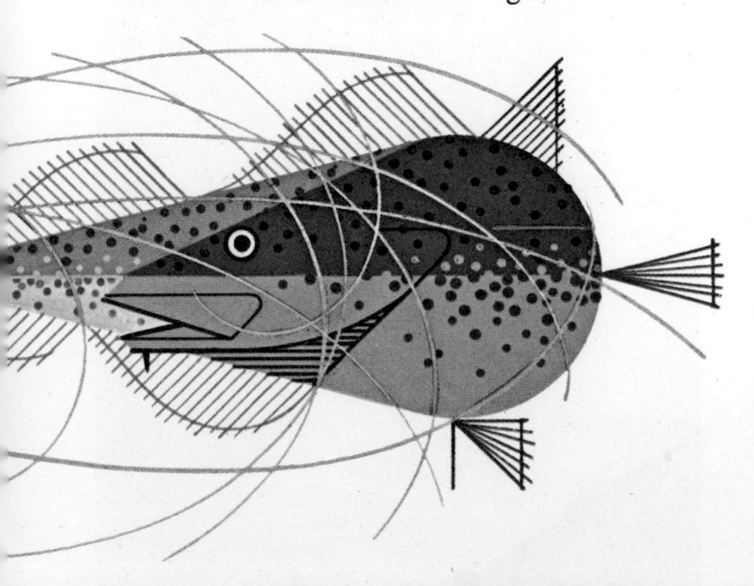

Sea cucumbers, the most unusual of the starfish's relatives, are surrounded by a tough, leathery skin. They look like sausages or, as their name implies, cucumbers. Unlike other members of this group, sea cucumbers do not have spines. Most sea cucumbers also lack tubefeet. They crawl along the bottom and burrow in the mud like worms. A ring of tentacles surrounds the mouth at one end of the body, and these are used to grab and push food inside. Generally they take in rich mud, digesting the food it contains and ejecting the remainder.

One giant sea cucumber attains a length of more than six feet. Orientals use dried sea cucumbers to make soup. Some sea cucumbers can break their body into a number of pieces when disturbed, each piece later becoming a new sea cucumber. They commonly eject their insides at intruders.

A calico scallop jets away from a prowling sea star.

Oysters, Clams, and Other Bivalves

An oyster will shut its shell when a shadow falls across it and will keep it closed until the shadow moves away. An oyster has no eyes, but cells lining the fleshy mantle surrounding its body are sensitive to light. Sometimes an oyster claps its shell shut so quickly that it makes a loud snap. Inquisitive ducks, foxes, and other animals have been trapped and drowned because they poked their nose into an oyster's shell. The alarmed oyster clamped down and stubbornly refused to let loose.

There are tales, too, of divers being drowned by a giant clam that lives in the South Pacific. This clam, largest of the mollusks, may weigh 500 pounds, its thick shell measuring as much as four feet across. Usually, the clam lives in shallow waters over coral reefs, and its shell stands so high above the bottom that even a wader would have to step extraordinarily high to get his foot inside. Islanders have used sharp pieces of the heavy shell to make tools and weapons. Pearls larger than golf balls are found inside a giant clam's shell, but they have no value.

Colonies of green algae grow in the soft, fleshy lining of the clam's shell and in the covering over its gills. The clam opens its shell and spreads this lining in the sun to put its built-in food factory to work.

Oysters and clams are among the more than 10,000 kinds of mollusks, or shellfish, that have a shell of two parts enclosing their soft body. They are called bivalves, and about two-thirds of the group live in the sea. Most kinds have a wedge-shaped muscular foot with which they crawl along or dig into the bottom. A few kinds, such as the oysters, do not have a foot; they are attached firmly by one shell to rocks, pilings or other objects.

Teredos, or shipworms, bore holes into wharves, wooden boats, or other wooden structures. Their shells may be no more than a quarter of an inch long, while the body of the wormlike animal is as much as two feet in length. Both of a teredo's shells are toothed in front, and they work like an auger as the animal rotates its body in its burrow.

An oyster clamps its shell shut on the nose of an inquisitive raccoon.

A shipworm grinds through a piece of piling to which a blue mussel is attached (above).

A herring gull drops a clam on the rocks to crack its shell and get the soft animal inside (right).

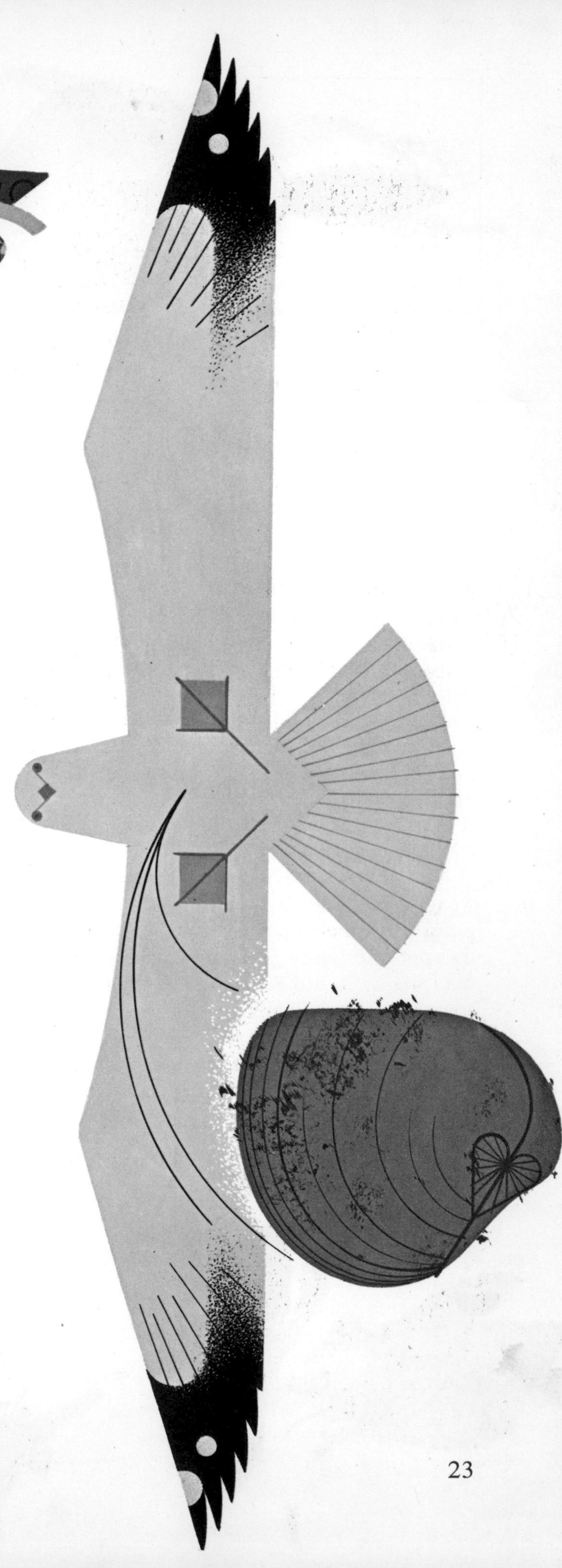

Mussels and clams that live in fresh-water streams, lakes, and ponds usually lie half buried in the sand or mud. The part of their shell sticking out is kept half open, and a current of water is drawn into the shell and over the gills. At the same time oxygen is being taken from the water, tiny plants and animals on which the mollusk feeds are being strained out. Pearl buttons are made from the thick mother-of-pearl lining of clam shells.

Gem pearls, the most prized products of bivalves, form when a grain of sand or some other foreign substance comes to lie between the shell and its fleshy lining. Layers of mother-of-pearl are secreted around the irritating particle, and in time a pearl is formed. Some pearls are blue, others black. The most valuable are the whitish-pink pearls produced by pearl oysters of the Pacific.

Around the edge of a scallop's mantle is a row of blue eyespots. Though a scallop appears to be as sluggish as a clam, it can swim rapidly by opening and closing its shell and jet-propelling itself through the water.

Scallops, clams, and oysters are one of man's largest harvests from the sea. Oysters are raised also on "farms." Young oysters, called spat, are spread over areas provided with old oyster shells or other objects on which they can settle and grow. In France, some oysters are reared in special pools in which a rich green alga grows and the oysters themselves become green. Of all the animal foods man eats, oysters and clams are among the very few eaten raw and alive.

Blue slug laying eggs

Giant African snail eating an orange

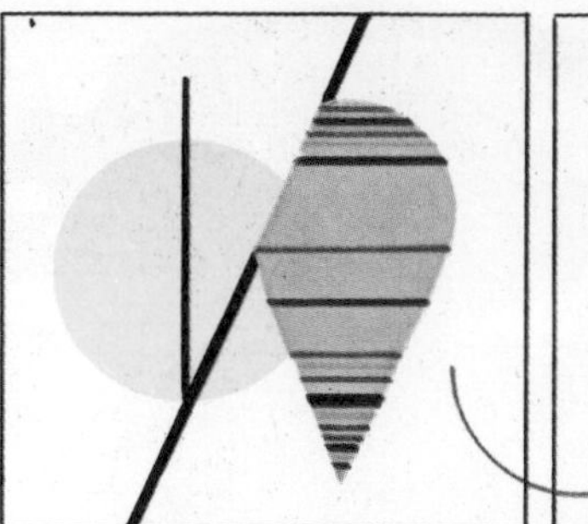

Tropical tree snail attached to twig

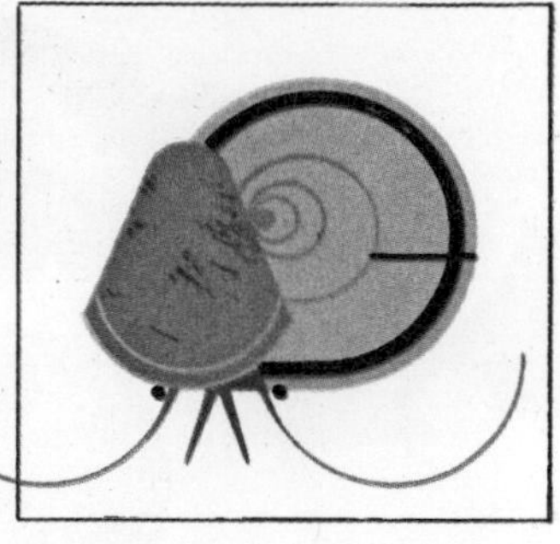

A common snail that lives in fresh water

Snails

The common garden snail creeps along on its slimy trail at a top speed of about ten feet an hour. No wonder a "snail's pace" refers to slow movement. When disturbed, the snail draws its blobbish body out of sight into its coiled, spiral shell. No one could imagine a less aggressive creature. But the sluggish, gentle garden snail has a flat, ribbon-like tongue studded with sharp-pointed teeth. It feeds on leaves and stems which it shreds by drawing its tongue back and forth over their surface like a file.

A snail can survive only in dampness. If the weather becomes dry, the snail secretes a slimy plug in its shell opening and waits inside for dampness to return. A drop of water on its shell may trigger it into action again, but the wait is sometimes long. Snails have been known to remain dormant for six years.

The some 40,000 kinds of snails form the largest group of mollusks, the gastropods. Gastropod means "stomach foot," as the muscular foot on which they crawl is directly beneath their soft inner organs. A typical gastropod has two pairs of tentacles that can be extended or withdrawn. At the end of one pair are eyes, probably sensitive only to movement.

The smallest land snails are so tiny that it takes nearly 30 shells lined side by side to measure an inch in length. Most beautiful are the tropical tree snails, some of which are found in the Everglades of southern Florida. Some of the snails that live in fresh-water ponds, swamps, and slow-moving streams are important as scavengers. They also serve as food for birds, fish, and other animals. They are put in aquariums to help clean the green scum off the glass sides.

Slugs are land-dwelling snails that do not have shells. Plump and slimy, they forage at night, leaving silvery trails wherever they crawl. Some slugs grow to a length of more than six inches and may be pests in flower and vegetable gardens.

Snails are most varied and abundant in the

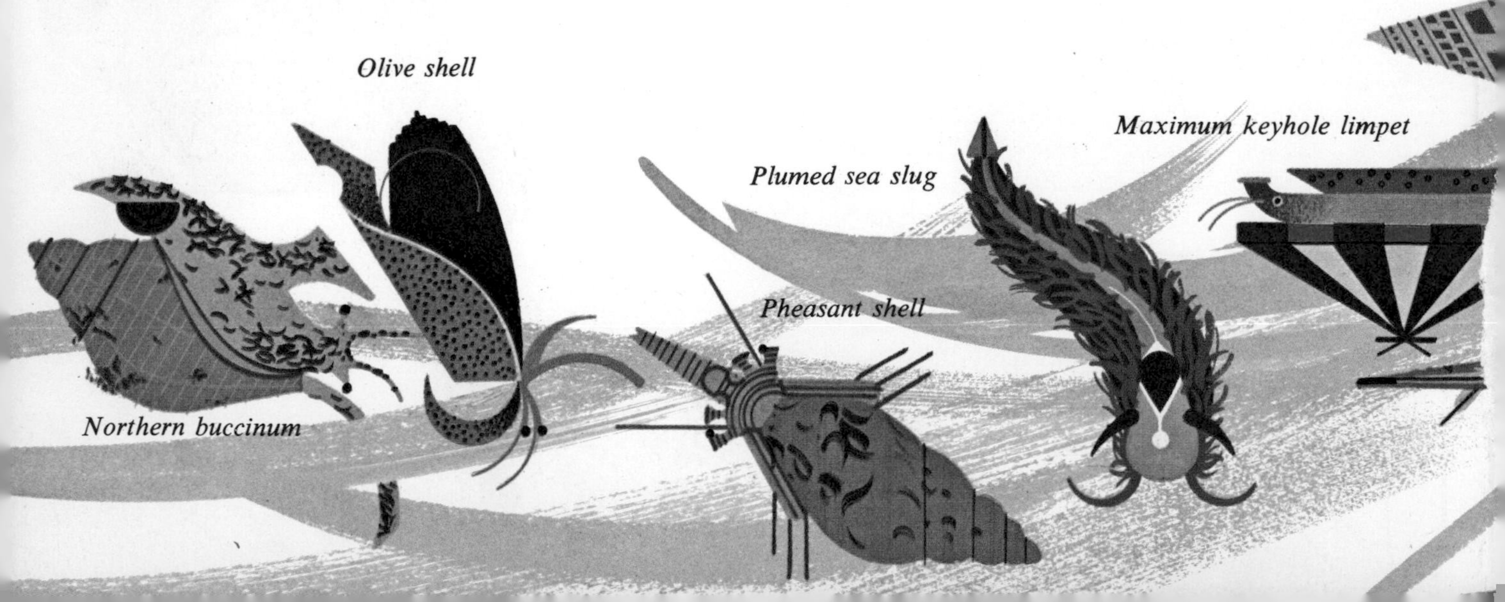

sea. Limpets and abalones have flattened shells, much like half of a clam shell. Limpets select a spot on a rock and scrape a depression into which their shell fits tightly. Sometimes a limpet travels ten feet or more as it feeds, but it always returns to home base to rest. Abalone shells, as much as ten inches long, are lined with thick iridescent mother-of-pearl from which jewelry and buttons are made. The muscular foot is cut into steaks or made into chowder.

Some of the tiny sea butterflies, most abundant in arctic waters, have paper-thin shells or no shells at all. Their foot is divided into two parts, like wings, and they paddle about on the surface of the sea in countless numbers.

Largest of the snails are the conchs, familiar as shell curios or as sea-food delicacies. The shells of some are a foot long and weigh as much as five pounds. A conch's slim foot has a daggerlike shelly tip that serves as a sword in battle and as a lid to close the opening to the shell. A conch uses its muscular foot as a springing device to hop along the bottom.

The stings of the beautiful cone shells, favorites with collectors, have been known to kill human beings. A cone releases half a dozen or more needle-sharp hollow harpoons from its snout. Each is connected to a poison sac. Normally the cone shell uses its poison to overcome small fish on which it feeds. Other sea snails bore holes through the thick, limy shells of oysters or other mollusks to get at the meat inside. Like their land-dwelling relatives, marine slugs lack shells, but their tentacles are plumed and colorful.

Collecting shells is a fascinating hobby. Turbans, top shells, periwinkles, cowries, helmet shells, murex, whelks, olive shells, volutes—these are among the many types sought after. Collectors may pay hundreds of dollars for perfect specimens.

A lobster dinner proves costly for an octopus when it finds itself being dined upon by the lobster (left). The many-tentacled chambered nautilus catches a shrimp (right).

Squids, Octopuses, and the Nautilus

For centuries seafaring men told frightening tales about a fantastic, many-armed marine monster that could hold a ship in one of its great, ropy arms while with its others it plucked the crew from the deck and devoured them. Norsemen called this fabulous creature the kraken and said that it measured more than a mile around its great body.

Unquestionably, the giant squid gave rise to these harrowing tales. Though the real animal is no match for the fables, it is nevertheless the largest of all animals without a backbone. Giant squids are known to measure 60 feet from the tip of their outstretched arms to the end of their torpedo-shaped body. Few have been seen alive, and little is known about their habits. They live on the continental slope, in water 600 or more feet deep.

Often sperm whales are found bearing scars from the suckers on the giant squid's arms. Each of the thousands of suckers, which measure two to three inches across, is rimmed with sharp hook-like teeth that dig deep into the whale's skin. But the squid is believed to be the loser in these unseen undersea struggles and is swallowed whole by the whale. Inside, the squid continues to fight and sinks its hooks into its captor's stomach wall, clinging tenaciously until the powerful digestive juices kill it.

Some of the more than 300 species of squids are less than an inch long. They live in the deep sea and, when disturbed, secrete a mucus that glows bluish-green. Other deep-sea squids have luminous organs on their body. The common Atlantic squid is known also as the sea arrow because of the arrow-like shape of its body as

A cuttlefish escapes a sand shark by ejecting an inky decoy, then turns pale itself and darts away.

it darts backward through the water. It is netted in large numbers for food and for bait.

When alarmed, some species of squids release a dark inky fluid. The purplish blob, resembling generally the squid's shape, hangs in the water as a decoy while the squid, which meantime has turned a much lighter color, darts away. The fluid is believed also to have an odor that confuses the pursuer.

Squids swim by shooting a spurt of water through a funnel-shaped tube on the underside of their body. The nozzle of the funnel can be directed forward, backward, or to either side to control the direction of movement. By this jet propulsion, a squid can streak through the water at 20 miles an hour. Some can leap from the water.

Octopuses have eight arms and no tentacles. Their body is round or sacklike. The smallest species of octopus measures only about two inches across its spread arms. The largest has a spread of more than 30 feet. The suckers on an octopus' arms lack teeth but have powerful suction cups. Prey is pulled to the mouth where it is bitten with the sharp, parrot-like beak. Some octopuses secrete a poison that kills their prey.

Most unusual of the octopuses is the paper nautilus, or argonaut. The female is about a foot long; the male less than an inch long. Unlike other octopuses, the female argonaut has a delicate shell, secreted between her first two arms. Inside this fragile float she carries her eggs.

Cuttlefish have a soft, spongy pen-shaped shell inside their body. This is the familiar cuttlebone used in bird cages. The largest cuttlefish, arms and all, is about five feet long. Cuttlefish are abundant in shallow inshore waters or swimming close to the surface offshore.

Millions of years ago the nautilus group of cephalopod mollusks was widespread and abundant. Now there are only a few kinds, all found in the South Pacific. A young nautilus' shell is hornshaped. Each time the nautilus grows larger, a new compartment is formed, sealed off from the previous chamber by a partition. The gas-filled, empty chambers make the many-compartmented shell so buoyant that the animal can move easily through the water. The animal lives in the last compartment.

Battles between the giant squid and the sperm whale are awesome sights.

Earthworms and Their Kin

A fisherman in Australia does not need to dig worms for bait. One worm will do, for a giant earthworm of that continent averages four feet in length. Exceptional worms may be more than ten feet long and four inches in diameter. The familiar garden earthworms of Europe and North America are only four to six inches long. The larger nightcrawlers may be a foot long.

It was Charles Darwin, most famous for his theory of evolution, who first focused the attention of scientists on the earthworm. Darwin discovered that as many as 50,000 worms might live in an acre of soil and that they performed a valuable service in turning or plowing the soil—from bottom to top. He estimated that the 50,000 worms would bring as much as 18 tons of soil to the top from three to five inches below the surface in just one year. Because earthworms keep the soil loose, water can soak in. The worms also eat decaying plant matter and turn it into rich humus.

Throughout the world there are some 2,000 species of earthworms. They are most abundant in grasslands which may harbor as many as a million worms to the acre. On the underside of each segment of an earthworm's body are tiny bristles, each moved by special muscles. The bristles anchor the worm as it crawls through or over the soil. Usually the worm crooks its head into a crevice or an irregularity in the soil, then draws the hind part of its body forward. In the soil, an earthworm eats its way forward. Earthworms may crawl on the surface at night, then return to their underground burrows when it is daylight.

An earthworm possesses both male and female sex organs. Nevertheless, earthworms mate and thus cross-fertilize their eggs. After mating, the orange band around the earthworm's body begins to slip forward. As it moves along, first eggs are deposited inside the band and then they are fertilized by sperm released from storage pockets in another segment. Finally the collar moves over the worm's head and drops to the ground as a

Earthworms plow the soil, and they also make meals for robins and moles.

seedlike cocoon. If conditions are right, the eggs soon hatch. But if it is too cold, too hot, or too dry, the eggs remain safe and unhatched inside the cocoon.

Earthworms are annelids, a name that refers to their ringed, segmented body. Not all earthworms are red. Some are cream-colored and threadlike; others are pink, and some are yellowish. And more than 200 kinds of annelids are bloodsucking parasites. These are the leeches of fresh-water streams, lakes, and ponds. Leeches wait in the mud or decaying vegetation at the bottom until a turtle, fish, human, or some other animal comes in contact with them. Then the leech grabs hold with the suckers at its head and tail and begins to take its meal by piercing the victim's flesh and pumping out blood. While food is available, a leech gorges, filling itself with three or four times its body weight in blood. Then it drops off and may not feed again for many months. It was once a common practise of medicine to "let blood"—that is, to draw out a patient's blood in the belief that this would rid him of his illness. The European leech used for the bloodletting measured from four to as much as eight inches long. One North American leech reaches a length of 18 inches. Some kinds of leeches are scavengers on the decaying remains of plants and animals rather than bloodsuckers.

Still other segmented worms live in the sea, from the seashore to depths of three miles. The paddle-like appendages on each segment of the greenish-blue clamworms serve not only for swimming but also as gills. When a clamworm finds prey, it quickly extends its strongly jawed proboscis and begins tearing its victim apart. Other seaworms live in tubes in the mud or sand of the seashore and feed on plant and animal foods that are swept through the tube. Some of the tubeworms have flower-like gills that stick from the head of the tube and wave in water. The plumes of some are orange, red, or purple and add to the bright colors of coral reefs. And one seaworm does not resemble a worm at all. Its body is oval and covered with long, grayish hairlike projections. Appropriately, it is called the sea mouse.

(1)

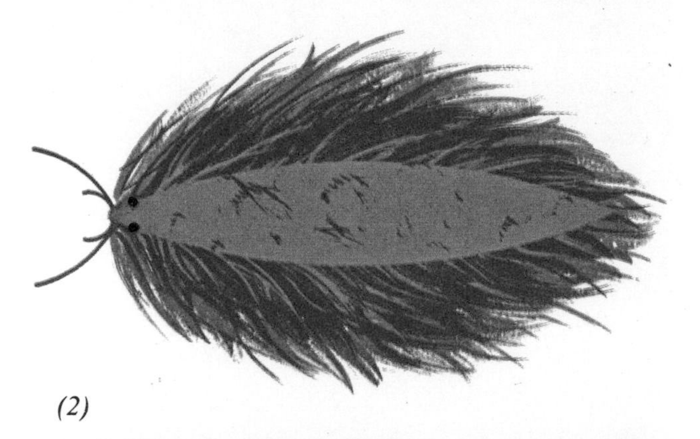
(2)

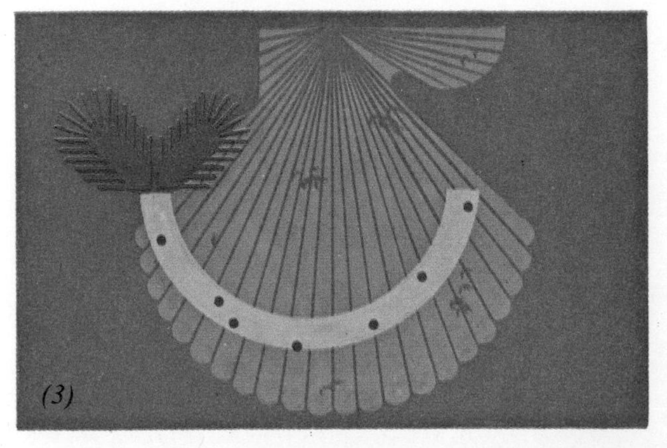
(3)

(4)

(1) A flounder eating a clamworm.
(2) A sea mouse, an unusual annelid.
(3) A colorful tubeworm fastened to a scallop shell.
(4) Pond leech on a bluegill sunfish.

A molting crayfish must keep hidden from enemies.

Crustaceans

To grow larger, the crayfish must shed its outer coat. Usually twice a year, the old shell splits down the back, and the crayfish crawls out. A freshly shed crayfish is soft and defenseless, a delicate morsel for turtles, fish, and other enemies. Until its new shell hardens, the crayfish hides under rocks or debris.

Most crayfish live in streams, ponds, or lakes, but a few kinds are found in wet lowlands where they dig burrows down to the water level. In dry weather, these "wells" may be as much as three feet deep. The dirt from the burrows is rolled into balls and carried to the surface, where it is piled around the entrance in conspicuous "chimneys."

All crayfish can crawl forward slowly, but they make their quick escapes by darting backward. The powerful thrust is achieved with a flip of the broad, muscular tail. If a pincer or leg breaks off, a new one grows in its place at the time of the animal's next molt.

Crayfish belong to the large group of animals known as arthropods, a name meaning "jointed legs." Insects, spiders, ticks, mites, centipedes, millipedes and scorpions are other arthropods. Crayfish are crustaceans, a group of some 25,000 species of arthropods, mostly marine.

Among the few land-dwelling crustaceans are sow bugs and pill bugs, which live under rocks, logs, or in other damp places. When disturbed, a pill bug rolls into a tight ball.

The most abundant of all crustaceans are nearly microscopic. Countless billions of these tiny segmented animals swarm in the sea. Some are enclosed in bivalved shells and look much like tiny clams. They are the food of menhaden, herrings, and many other fishes. The blue whale feeds exclusively on krill, which are small crustaceans.

The crayfish's counterpart in salt water is the lobster. The largest, which lives in the cool inshore waters of the Atlantic, may attain a length of more than two feet and a weight of 30 pounds. Spiny or rock lobsters of warm waters are smaller and lack claws but have instead a formidable array of spines on their legs, antennae, and body.

A young barnacle swims freely, like other crustaceans, but the adults are attached plantlike to rocks, pilings, the hulls of ships, or other firm objects. A barnacle's heavy shell is composed of half a dozen separate plates; the animal inside, with a segmented body and legs, rests head down, its legs sticking out and kicking continually to cause a current of food-laden water to flow into the shell.

The prize human food among the crustaceans is shrimp. More than 100 million pounds are harvested every year from United States waters. Among the most interesting are the snapping or pistol shrimp of warm waters. A plunger and cylinder structure on their claw is used to make a loud snapping noise that stuns small animals nearby.

Crabs are another familiar group of crustaceans. Land crabs may raid coastal vegetable gardens or field crops and are commonly seen scurrying along highways. The large, powerful robber crab of the South Pacific is reported to climb coconut trees, cut down the heavy fruit, and then husk them. Blue crabs, a prized sea food, are abundant in the shallows and sometimes wander into bays or up rivers in warm months. Male fiddler crabs have one claw twice to nearly three times the size of the other. When a male courts a female, he sits near the burrow he has dug in the mud or sand and waves this large claw. Sometimes it looks as though he is fiddling.

The hermit crab uses its thick front claws to close the opening to the abandoned seashell in which it lives. The hermit crab's hind pair of legs are claspers that anchor the crab in its shell. When the crab becomes too large for its shell, it selects a larger one. Giant sea crabs of Japanese waters measure as much as 12 feet across their legs. Heavy-bodied crabs of Alaskan waters, measuring as much as four feet in leg span, have become a popular sea food.

Sand fleas or sand bugs burrow into the sand at the tide line. These popular fish baits resemble the related trilobites that were abundant in the seas some 400 million years ago and that are known today only as fossils.

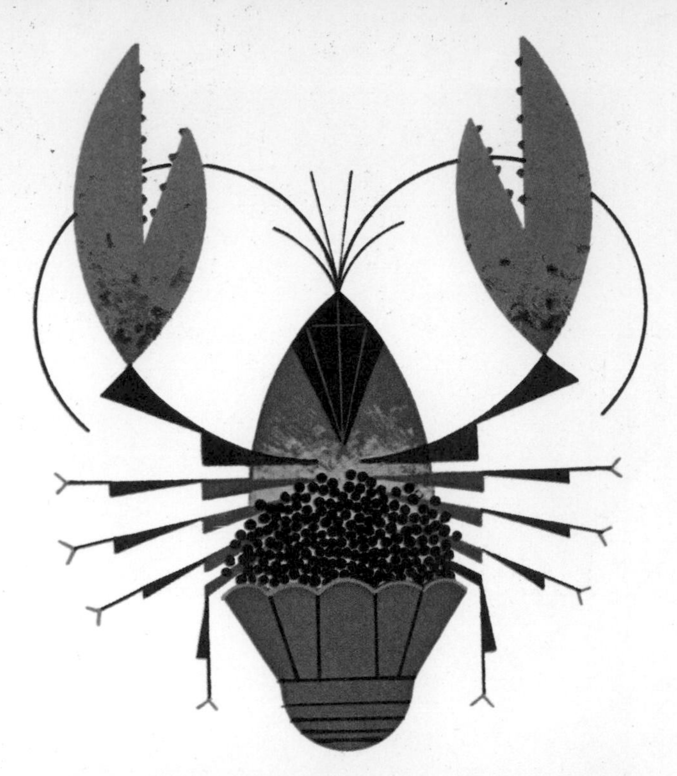

Like crayfish, the female lobster carries her eggs in a berry-like cluster until they hatch.

Gooseneck barnacles, their feet kicking, attached to a piece of driftwood (above). The scrappy blue crab (below) will attack any intruder, no matter what its size.

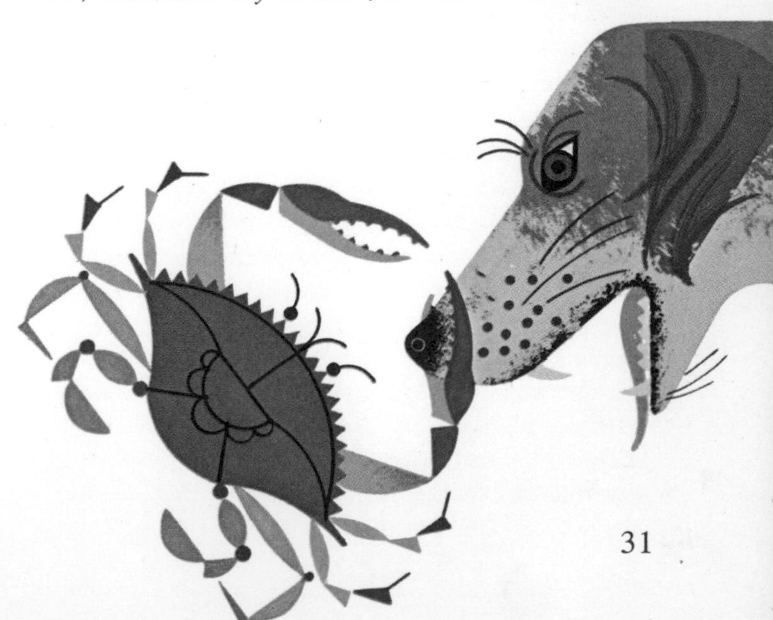

A hummingbird becomes a tarantula's victim.

Spiders, Ticks, and Scorpions

Early in the 1700's a woman naturalist painted a picture of a giant, hairy tarantula crouched over the body of a colorful tropical hummingbird on the limb of a calabash tree in the Amazon. The bird apparently had been captured while incubating its eggs, shown in a nest nearby. The most learned scientists of the day scoffed at Madam Maria Merian's painting, for no one believed that a bird-hunting spider really existed.

Nearly a hundred years later the English naturalist Henry Bates confirmed Maria Merian's observation, for in his travels through the Amazon country, he also saw these spiders with their bird victims. Many others have seen them since. Some of these big tropical tarantulas measure nearly 10 inches across their spread legs. At night they come out of hiding to stalk and kill their prey. Mostly they hunt insects, but they may also kill and devour animals as large as birds, lizards, or small rodents.

Because of their gargantuan size and formidable appearance, tarantulas, though truly skulking creatures, are among the most feared of all spiders. They can bite severely with their large fangs, but their poison is no more potent than the sting of a bee. Their hairs cause an irritating itch when they touch the skin.

In southwestern United States, tarantulas and their close relatives, the trapdoor spiders, are victims themselves of a smaller, fearless insect—the tarantula hawk, a metallic blue wasp. The female wasp methodically hunts and attacks these large spiders, stinging a victim again and again until it is paralyzed. Then she drags the giant into a burrow, already dug, and lays an egg on its abdomen. When the egg hatches, the wasp's larva feeds on the still-living spider.

Spiders generally are among man's best friends, though few animals are more feared or misunderstood. Most spiders are insect eaters and may destroy large numbers of flies, mosquitoes, and other annoying or disease-carrying pests. Spiders differ from insects in having four pairs of legs, rather than three, and by their lack of wings. They are widely distributed land dwellers. Though they are air breathers, some have developed the remarkable ability to remain submerged for long periods, possibly several weeks. They breathe oxygen trapped in a bubble surrounding their abdomen. Other spiders can run swiftly over the surface of water without sinking.

Nearly all of the more than 30,000 kinds of spiders kill their prey with a poison injected from their fangs. They then suck out the soft parts of the body or lather their victim with digestive juices to liquefy it before taking it into their body. If they catch an animal too large to kill with one bite, many spiders will wrap the victim in silk to stop its struggles while they continue to bite until it dies. Only a few kinds have a poison powerful enough to do serious harm to human beings. The most dangerous of these is the black widow.

Wolf spiders and jumping spiders are active hunters. They stalk their prey and then attack swiftly by running or jumping. Others, such as the crab spiders, are camouflaged by their color to look much like the flower on which they wait for prey to approach. Trapdoor spiders hide in silk-lined burrows, some of which are equipped with a hinged, earthen door. They come out on hunting forays but take refuge quickly, holding their door tightly shut, when pursued by lizards or other predators.

Spiders are best known, though, for catching their prey in silken webs. The very name spider, in fact, can be traced to words meaning "spinner," referring to the spinning of webs. The spider's

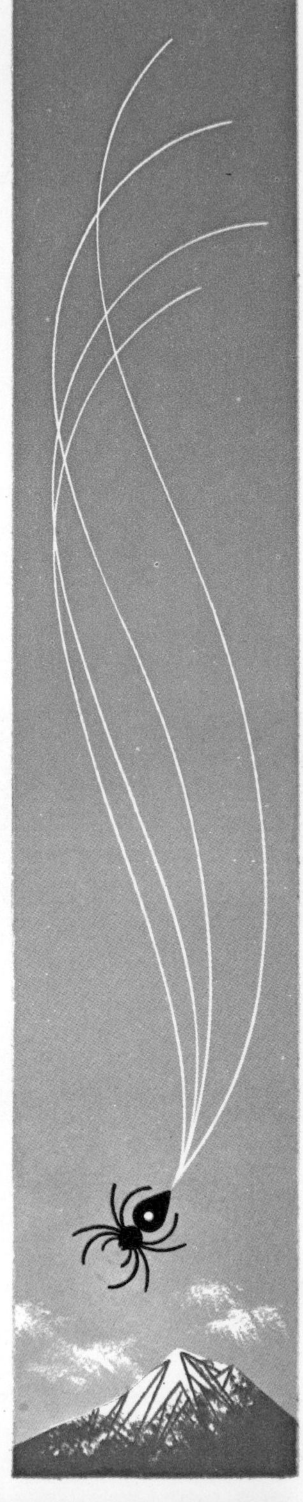

An orb-weaving garden spider spins its web (top left).

A young spider's silk parachute carries it long distances (top right).

A female black widow spider wraps her paralyzed prey, a harlequin bug, in silk (bottom).

silk, produced by glands in its abdomen, is secreted as a liquid that hardens the instant it is exposed to air. Silk is strong and stretchable. In some of the finest strands, it may be no more than a millionth of an inch in diameter.

Some spiders make sheetlike webs. The very large sheets of a group of spiders living in warm climates throughout the world sometimes measure several yards across, and the silk is so strong it can trap and hold birds. Pacific islanders use silk from these webs to make fishnets. Spiders that build sheetlike webs may rest on the underside of their snare or hide in a silken tunnel at one end of the web. They run quickly toward a disturbance that signals a catch.

Web-spinning is best developed in the orb weavers, such as the common yellow-and-black garden spider. Heavy non-sticky lines radiate

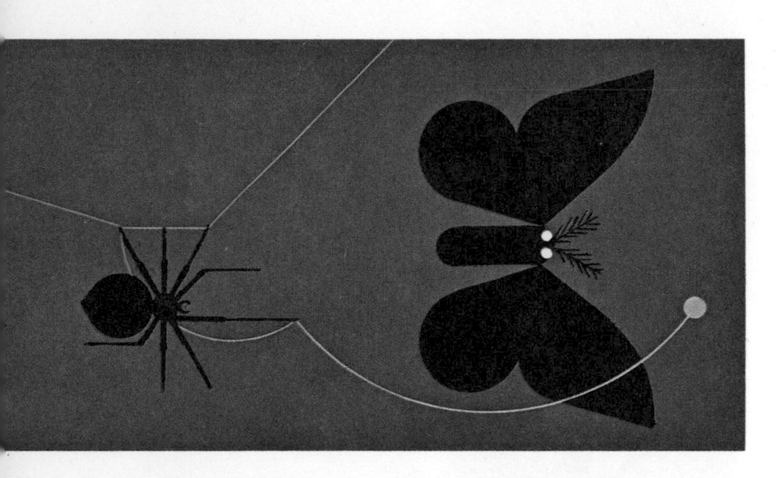

A bolas spider catches a passing moth by throwing a sticky ball attached to a strand of silk.

from a hub where the spider commonly rests. Spiraling around this framework are thinner, sticky lines that catch and hold flies and other insects. The spider travels along the non-sticky lines to retrieve its catch. A broken web is quickly repaired, or in some cases, a new web is spun every night.

Spiders use their silk in many and characteristic ways. They spin silken sacs for their eggs and nursery webs for their young. As they crawl, they let out a dragline behind, anchoring it at intervals, and let themselves down from high places on silken lines. Some young spiders travel long distances by "ballooning" on strands of silk.

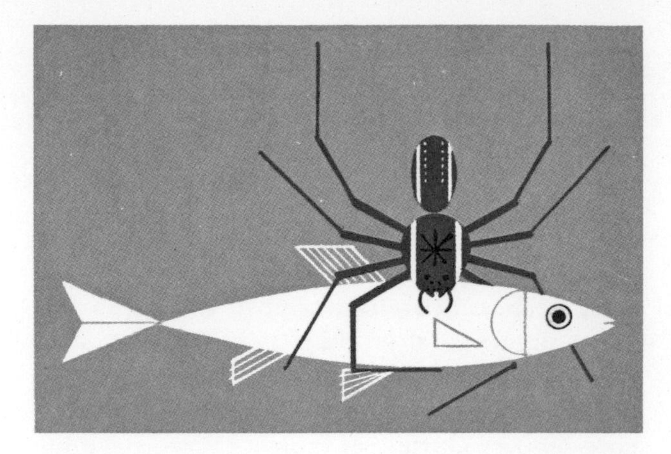

Diving spiders are known to catch and eat small minnows.

In the fall, the young spiders climb to the tips of plants or high onto rocks or other elevations. Then they pay out a thread of silk, the gossamer threads of literature. When the strand blowing in the wind is long enough, it drags the spider from its perch. Ballooning spiders have been found several miles above the surface of the earth and hundreds of miles at sea.

Ticks, which belong to the same class of animals as spiders, are bloodsucking parasites of birds, mammals, and other animals. A tick's body swells to several times normal size when it has gorged on a victim's blood. Rocky mountain spotted fever is one of several dangerous diseases transmitted by ticks. Mites, closely related to ticks, are very small animals abundant in soil and water and as parasites of plants and animals. Some mites cause swellings, or galls, on leaves

A trapdoor spider emerges from its burrow to capture a tiger beetle.

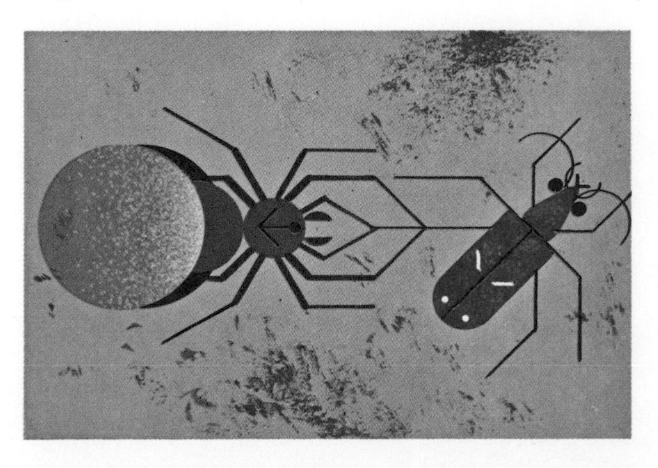

and stems. A plant wilts and dies as its juices are sucked out when infested with large numbers of mites. Chiggers, the bane of grassy places in summer, are tiny red mites. Mites are responsible, too, for mange and other itches.

Scorpions, most abundant in deserts and in the tropics, have a slim, segmented body with a poisonous stinger at its tip. Some kinds are highly dangerous. Scorpions hunt at night and use their sting to paralyze their prey. If they rest in clothing, shoes, or other places, they may be picked up or stepped on accidentally. Young scorpions are carried on their mother's back for several weeks before they venture forth on their own.

Whip scorpions and pseudoscorpions look much like real scorpions but do not have a stinger in their tail. Daddy longlegs, or harvestmen, are closely related harmless creatures common around houses or in debris. Like whip scorpions, they give off a foul, sour odor when picked up.

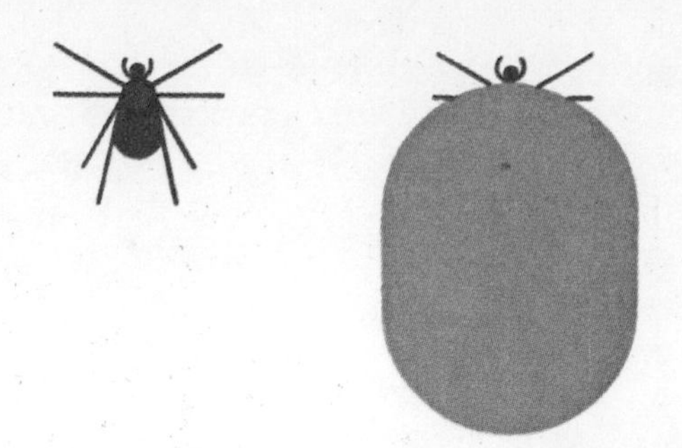

A tick before and after it has eaten its meal of blood.

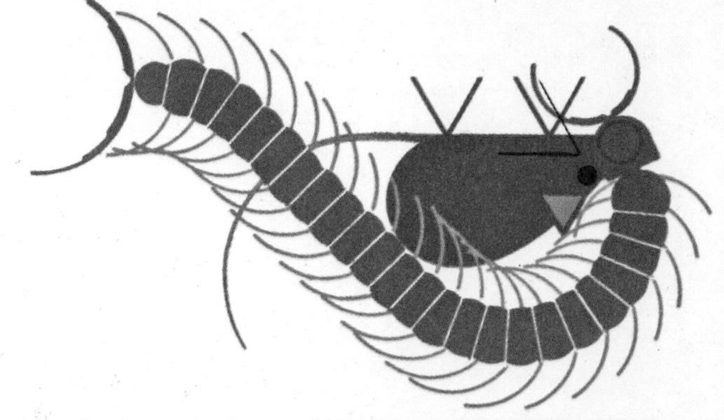

Tropical centipede catching a mouse.

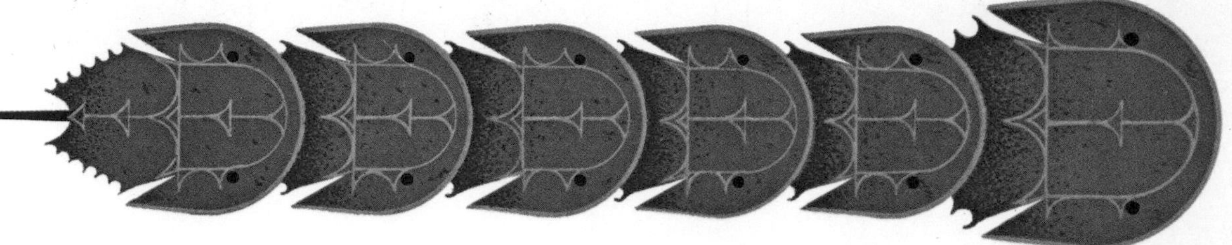

A female horseshoe crab towing a train of males at mating time.

One of the most unusual of the spider relatives is a "living fossil," the sole survivor of a group that was most prominent millions of years ago. This is the horseshoe crab, common in the shallow waters along the Atlantic coast, in the Gulf of Mexico, and in the western Pacific. Large horseshoe crabs are nearly two feet long. They crawl slowly over the bottom and feed on soft-bodied animals. Sometimes large numbers appear on the beaches. They are harmless, but their shells are covered with protective spikes and their long tail is stiff and pointed.

Centipedes and millipedes are land-dwellers with many-segmented bodies. Millipedes ordinarily have two pairs of legs on each segment; centipedes have only one pair. Centipedes are swift hunters. Millipedes crawl about slowly and curl into a ball to escape enemies. A tropical centipede is nearly a foot long.

Young scorpions ride on their mother's back.

Harvestmen have slim, fragile legs.

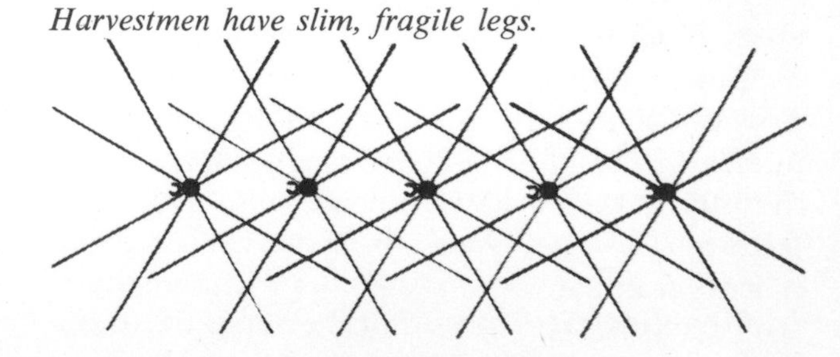

Insects

Insects are in many ways unquestionable rulers of the animal world. Certainly it is true in numbers. Nearly a million different species of insects have been named so far, and some scientists say the final total will be close to 10 million.

The number of individuals is truly beyond counting. The weight of all the insects in the world is said to be greater than the weight of all other animals combined. One acre of rich forest land has been estimated to support an insect population of 65 million. A single colony of ants or termites may contain as many as a million individuals, and many such colonies can be found on only a few acres. In plague years, seething clouds of locusts, or grasshoppers, may extend over hundreds of square miles. The earth is scoured of vegetation in their path, and where the migrating mass is most dense, the sky is darkened on even the sunniest day. In times of mayfly hatches in the Great Lakes region, these fragile, short-lived insects are attracted to city lights in such large numbers that snow plows must be used to clear the streets. Mosquitoes have been known to clog the nostrils of grazing cattle and cause them to suffocate.

Each of the principal groups, or orders, of insects has features unlike those of any other. Beetles form the largest group, with more than 250,000 kinds. In nearly all beetles, the front pair of wings is hard. They are a protective cover over a pair of thin, hind wings, which are folded beneath when not used in flight. There are approximately 100,000 kinds of butterflies and moths, identified by the thin overlapping scales in attractive colors and designs over their broad wings. Flies, forming another group of about

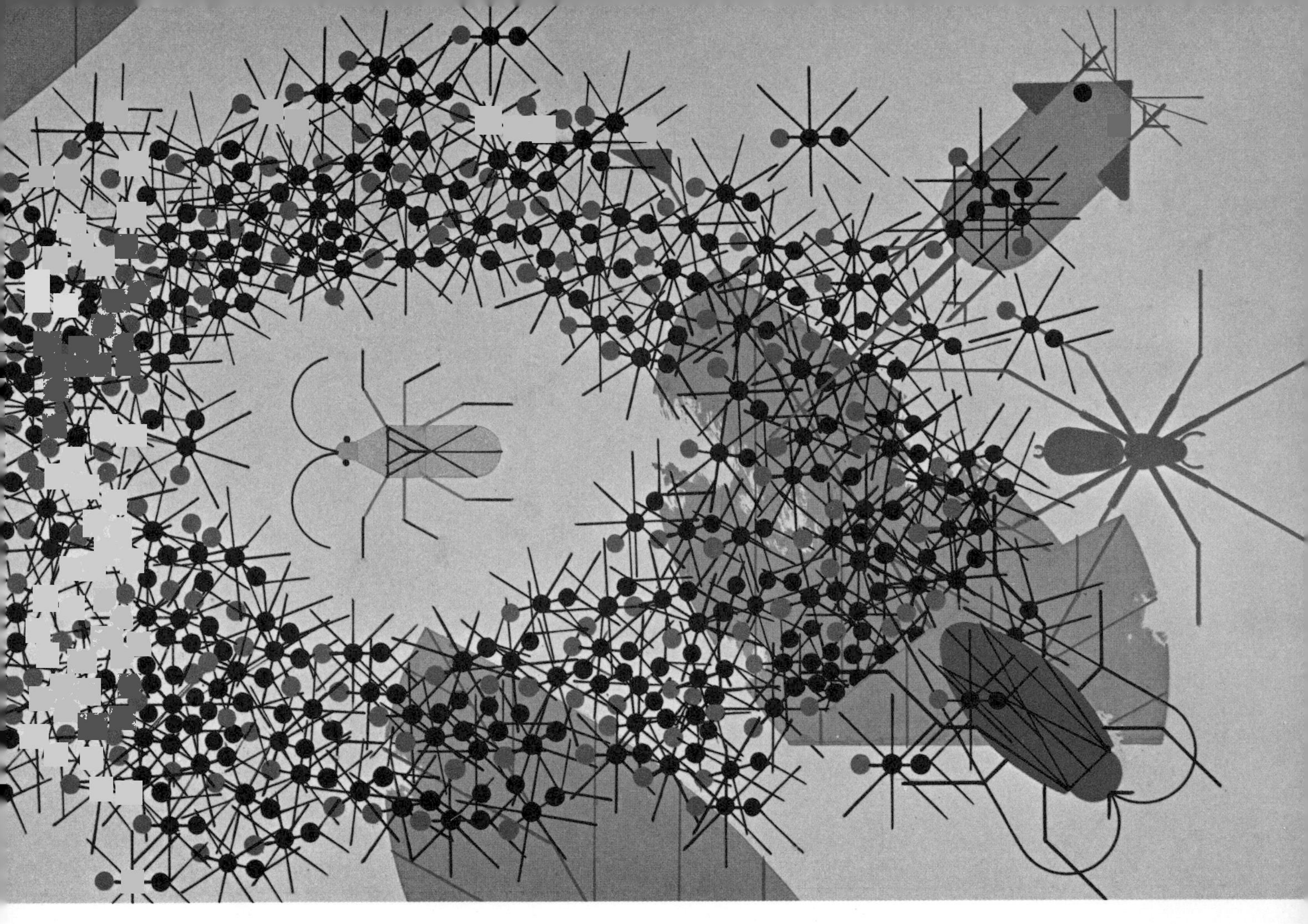

Army ants overrun a coral snake, bypass a stinkbug, then attack a fleeing mouse, a wolf spider, and a roach.

100,000 kinds, have only one pair of wings. Their hind wings have become knoblike balancers. Most ants do not have wings, but some ants and the bees and wasps that are members of the same group have two pairs of glass-clear wings. Many members of this order, containing some 100,000 kinds, live in complex social groups and are generally ranked as the most advanced of all the insects. Grasshoppers, crickets, cockroaches, and praying mantids form a small group in which all have narrow straight-edged front wings. In their winged form, termites have two pairs of wings of equal size. Winged ants are similar in appearance, but their wings are not of equal size. Also termites have no "waist," or narrowed area, between their thorax and abdomen; ants have a distinct waist.

True bugs form an important group of some 25,000 kinds. The base of a bug's front wings is thick; the hind portion is membranous. True bugs, including some of the most damaging pests, feed by piercing the tissues of a plant or an animal and sucking out the fluids. Aphids, leaf hoppers, scale insects, and cicadas belong to a closely related group. Other small orders of insects are those containing the dragonflies and damselflies, fleas, lice, mayflies, and lacewings.

Insects are most colorful, bizarre, and varied in the tropics, but almost no place on earth is without insects. Some kinds hop about on the snow of glacial fields high in the mountains or in the Arctic. The wriggling maggots of some kinds of flies develop in springs in which the water temperature is over 100 degrees. Others live in stagnant water or even in pools of oil, breathing through long tubes that stick above the surface. There are kinds of insects that can bore through lead cables and others that thrive on diets of opium, wood, tobacco, dried hides, hot spices, and similar unusual substances. Insects live in hot, dry deserts and in deep caves. A few kinds of mosquitoes and other flies develop only in salt marshes or in the even brinier waters of salt lakes. One kind of water strider, similar to those seen skating about on fresh-water ponds, lives on the surface of the sea, often many miles from land.

The typical insect's body is divided into three parts: head, thorax, and abdomen. Attached to its head is a pair of antennae, or feelers. Most insects have one pair of compound eyes, each composed of numerous simple eye units—as many as 25,000 in the dragonflies. In addition, most insects also have one to several simple eyes, usually located between the compound eyes. Insects are probably able to detect even slight movements easily, but they are nearsighted and cannot distinguish the shapes of objects well. Attached to an insect's thorax are three pairs of jointed legs, and most insects have two pairs of wings.

In the many kinds of insects, there are many exceptions to these basic features, of course. There are, for example, wingless insects. The legs of the different kinds of insects may be adapted for jumping, running, digging, holding prey, or other uses. The antennae may be plumed, club shaped, toothed, or in various other shapes. But one or all of these features serve to distinguish insects from such closely related types of animals as spiders. Spiders, for example, have only two body divisions, no wings, and four pairs of legs.

Like other jointed-legged animals, or arthropods, an insect's skeleton is outside its body. This tough outer skin is made of a substance much like that in your fingernails. Over some parts of the body it forms a thick armor, but at leg joints and other movable parts it is thin and flexible.

Along the sides of the insect's body are holes, called spiracles, through which it breathes. Each hole is the opening for a network of tubes that are divided again and again until they are microscopic. They extend throughout the insect's body.

Primitive dragonflies that soared over the ancient coal-forming swamps some 400 million years ago were the largest insects that have ever lived. Their wings spanned nearly two and a half feet. One of the giants of today is a South American moth with a wingspread of more than 12 inches. The bulky African goliath beetle measures nearly eight inches long, and a slim Asiatic walkingstick, related to the praying mantid, is about 15 inches long. At the opposite extreme, in a range of sizes unequalled in the animal world, are beetles so tiny that a hundred of them lined up end to end measure only an inch long. Flies of one group spend most of their lives as parasites inside the eggs of other insects. Even the largest insects are small compared to most other animals. The small size is to their

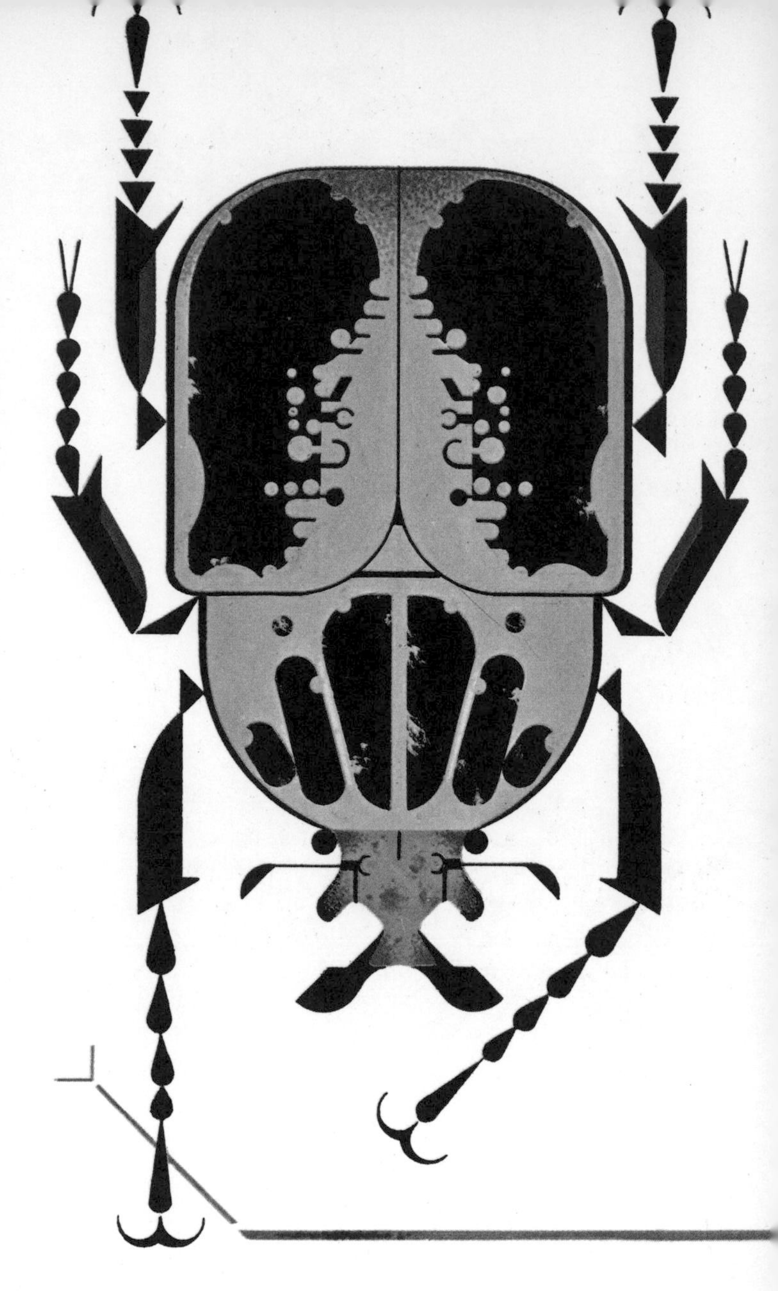

African goliath beetle is one of the heaviest of insects.

advantage, for a small animal has less difficulty finding enough food or a place to hide.

In some groups of insects, the young that hatches from the egg looks like the adult and has similar habits. These young, called nymphs, do not have wings, but if the adults are winged, then the buds of wings soon appear and increase in size each time the nymph sheds. The wings are fully developed by the time the nymph becomes an adult. Grasshoppers, crickets, and cockroaches are among the common insects that are at first nymphs. Their change in form is called metamorphosis. In those insects with nymph stages, the change is gradual, with only three development stages; egg, nymph, and adult.

Many other insects have four stages in their life history. These are the egg, larva, pupa, and adult. Fruit flies may go through all four of their life stages in only a few days. Some of the cicadas require as long as 17 years to complete their development. These insects change greatly in appearance and habits at each stage. They are said to have a complete metamorphosis. A caterpillar is the larval stage of a butterfly or a moth. It is wormlike and has chewing mouthparts; the adult has scaly wings, a much smaller body, and a long tubular mouth used to sip nectar. Beetle larvae are known commonly as grubs, while the larvae of flies are called maggots.

The remarkable changes that transform larvae into their quite different adult form occur during the pupa stage. Often the pupa is called the "resting stage," but at no period of an insect's life is internal activity greater. Also, some kinds of pupae are able to wriggle their way through loose soil or along tunnels in wood, and the pupae of some species can swim. In some insects the change from larva to adult requires only a few days; in others, the change takes months. Many kinds of insects pass the winter months as pupae.

Many grasshoppers, beetles, bees, and others make sounds as they fly, either by the rattling vibration of their wings or by the rubbing of one wing against the other. Katydids and crickets rub their wings together when not in flight, and some grasshoppers draw their hind legs over roughened areas on their wings. Cicadas produce their shrill sounds by vibrating thin, oval membranes on each side of their body.

Some insects pick up sounds with the sensitive hairs scattered over their body. Others have definite "ears." A katydid's ears are located on each front leg and are quite conspicuous. A cricket's ears are on its front legs, too, but are small slits,

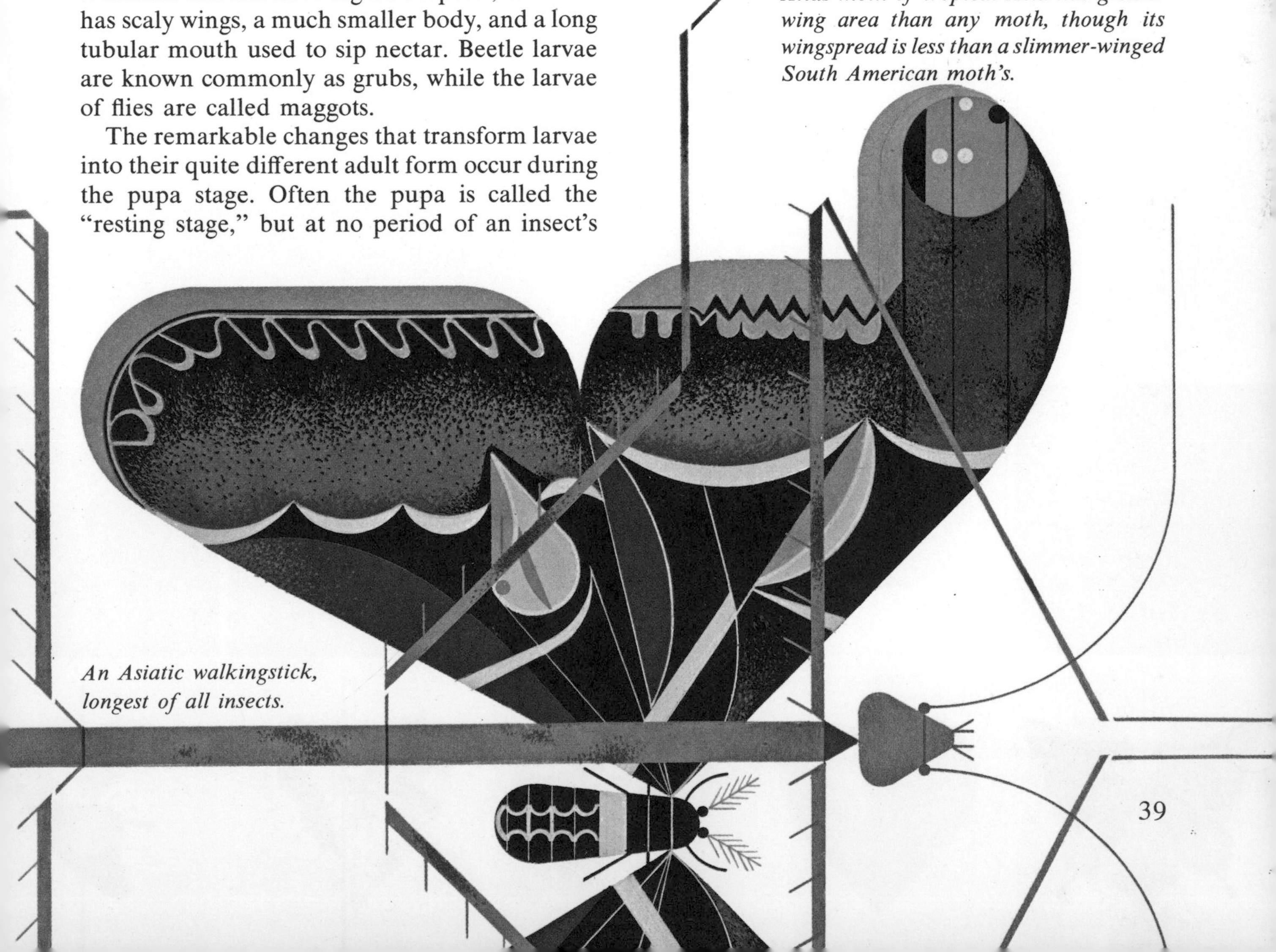

Atlas moth of tropical Asia has greater wing area than any moth, though its wingspread is less than a slimmer-winged South American moth's.

An Asiatic walkingstick, longest of all insects.

not as easy to see. Other insects have ear membranes on the sides of their body.

Some kinds of insects are so beneficial that man could not survive long without them. There would be no fruit and vegetable crops if insects did not fertilize their flowers. Insects visit these flowers to get food, either the sweet nectar or rich pollen. In the process, they transfer pollen grains to the flower's ovary.

Most important of the pollinators are the bees and flies. Honeybees have special stiff hairs on their legs for carrying pollen, and with their long tongue they can reach deep into the flower for nectar. Insects active during the day may be attracted to flowers of a particular color. Night-feeding moths are the chief pollinators of the sweet-smelling flowers that are located mainly by odor. Many flowers are shaped in such a way that it is easy for insects to land on them and to pick up pollen. It is also almost impossible for them to leave without brushing pollen onto the top of the tube leading to the ovary of the flower.

Honey and wax are valuable products that come from insects. Natural silk is obtained by unraveling the thin threads spun by caterpillars of the silkworm moth when they make their cocoons. Shellac is produced by lac insects as a protective secretion over their body, and cochineal is a red dye made from the crushed bodies of a scale insect. Insects are the principal food of many kinds of birds, fishes, and other animals. In some parts of the world, people eat insects, too. They are a rich source of protein.

House flies, fleas, lice, and cockroaches are among the kinds of insects that have been associated with man and his domestic animals, pets, plants and their products for centuries. Some of these insects owe their abundance, widespread distribution and perhaps even their survival to their close association with man. Clothes moths, for example, feed only on wool, fur, and other animal products. Without man these substances would be harder to find. Many pests of plants have profited, too, by man's methods of farming. The Colorado potato beetle was an inconspicuous insect that fed on a plant that grew only in the Rocky Mountains. Not until settlements

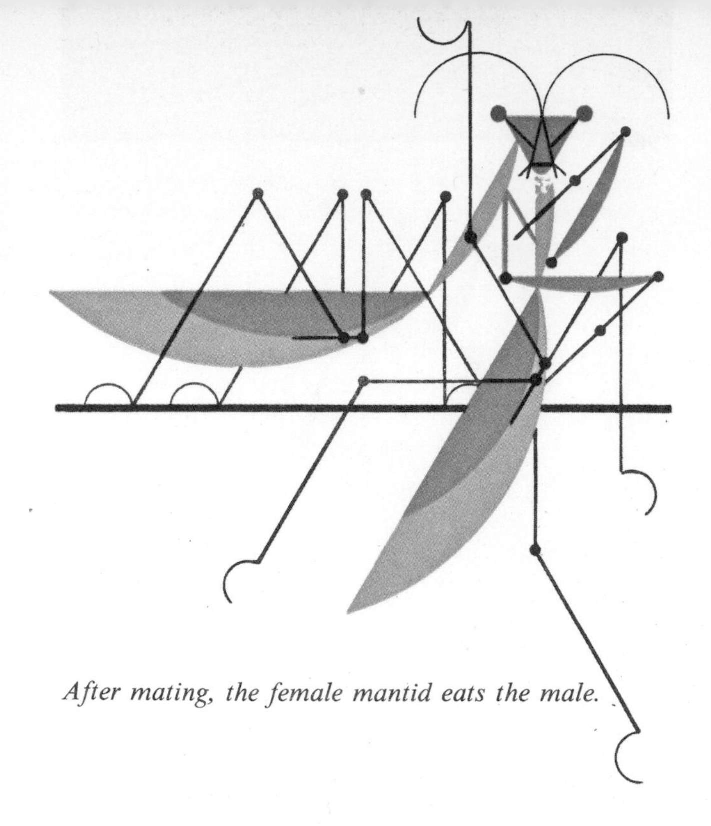

After mating, the female mantid eats the male.

Simple metamorphosis of a katydid

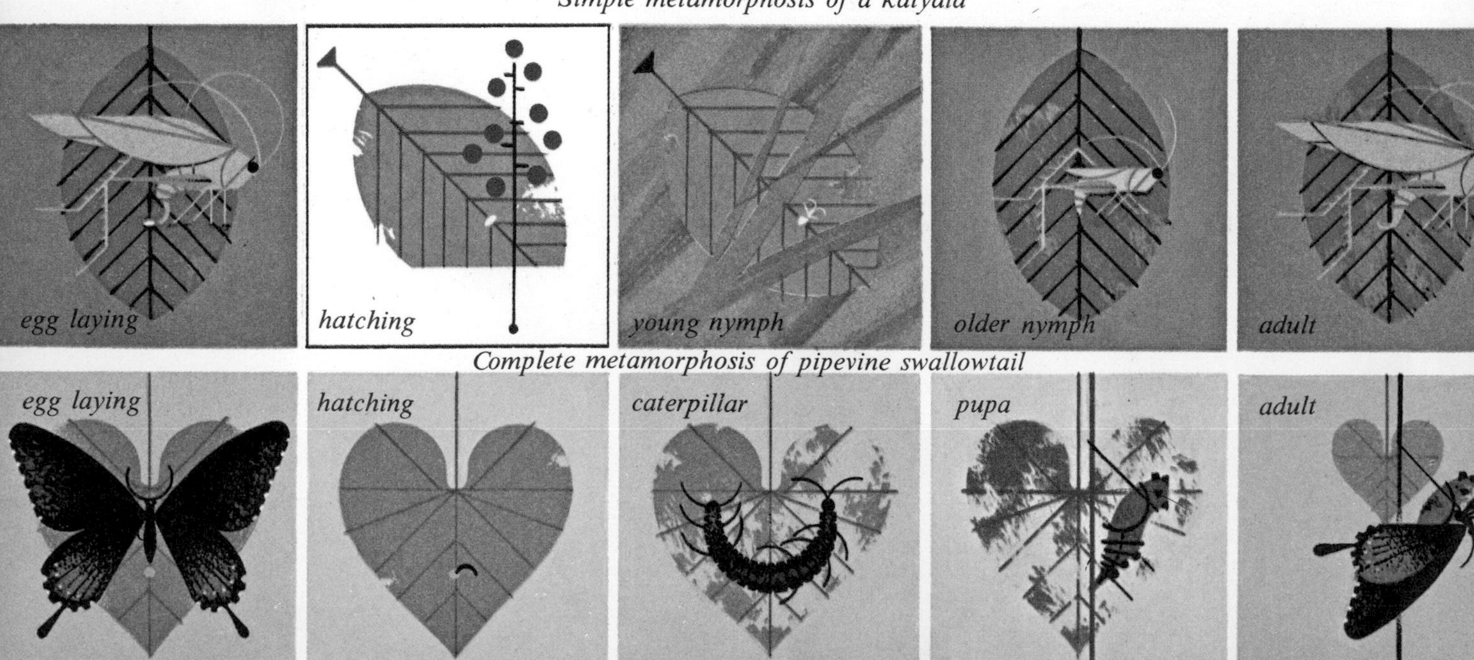

Complete metamorphosis of pipevine swallowtail

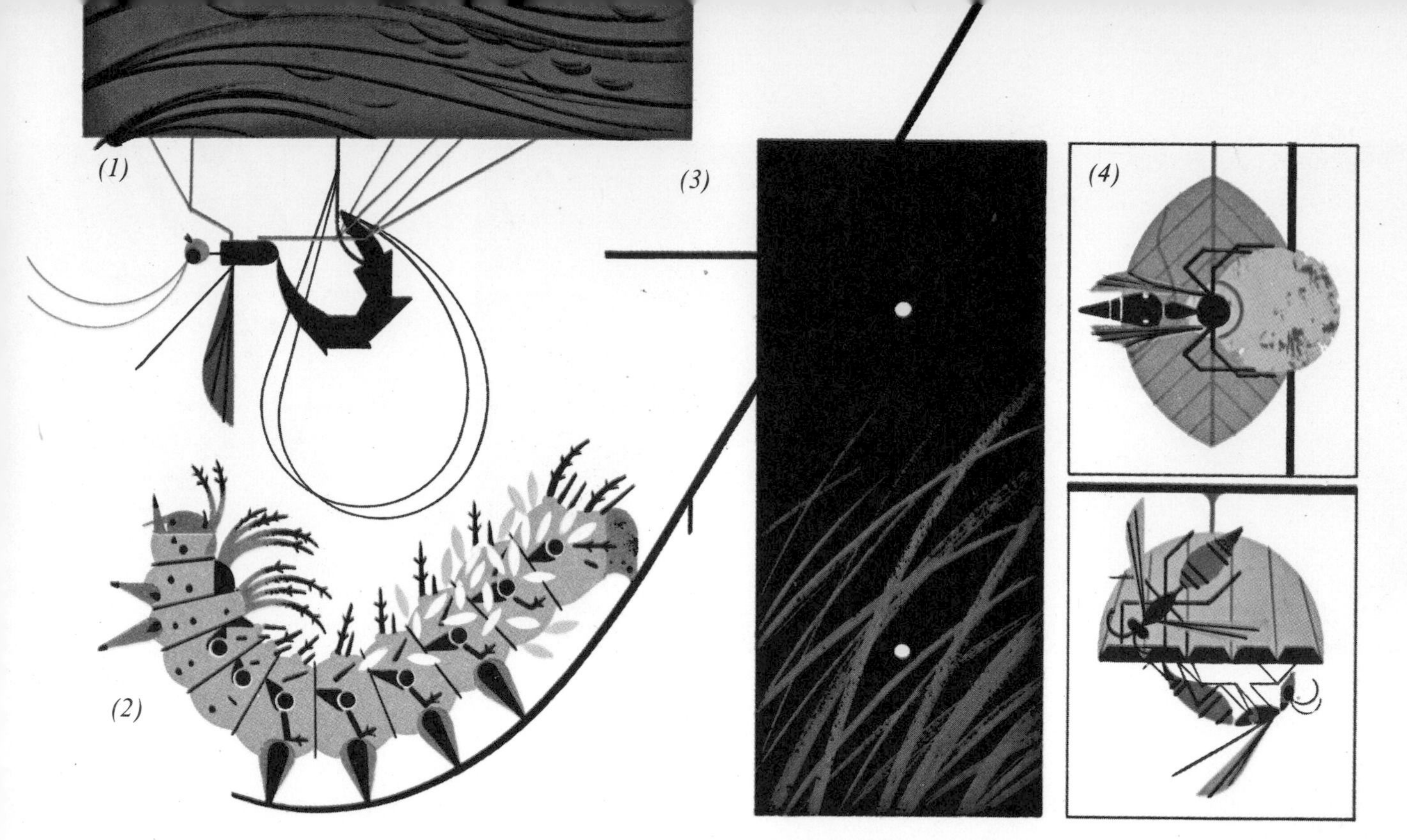

(1) A female ichneumon wasp pierces wood with her ovipositor to lay eggs in a beetle's larva.
(2) A hickory horned devil (the caterpillar of the royal walnut moth), with cocoons of parasitic braconid wasp.
(3) Fireflies use their light to signal mates.
(4) Potter wasp and nest above; paper wasp and nest below.

spread to the Rocky Mountains did the beetle gets its taste of the cultivated potato. The beetles then spread eastward from potato patch to potato patch.

The few kinds of insects that are really harmful have a greater effect on man's health and welfare than do any other group of animals. Insects compete strongly with man for food and living space. In the United States, the damage they do amounts to about four billion dollars every year. Insects destroy an estimated 10 percent of all crops in the field, then continue to destroy them in storage. They eat the wood of buildings and cause them to collapse. No plant or plant product is immune to their attack. Despite the use of modern chemicals to kill insect pests, none has ever been totally eliminated.

Burying beetles bury a dead mouse on which they will lay eggs. Larvae will feed on carcass.

Among the most damaging are insects that carry diseases. Fleas that lived on rats spread the Black Death, or bubonic plague, throughout Europe in the 14th century. An estimated 150 million people died of this disease. Yellow fever, passed to man by the bites of mosquitoes, had to be conquered before the Panama Canal could be dug. In both World War I and World War II, casualties due to disease-carrying insects were greater than from enemy bullets. Malaria, a mosquito-carried disease, is to this day the world's major health problem.

A honeybee may fly a wandering, zigzag course in its search for nectar, but it returns to the colony by the shortest direct route. There it does a tail-wagging dance that tells other workers how far and which direction to travel and whether the source of nectar is rich.

Insects, even honeybees, are not intelligent

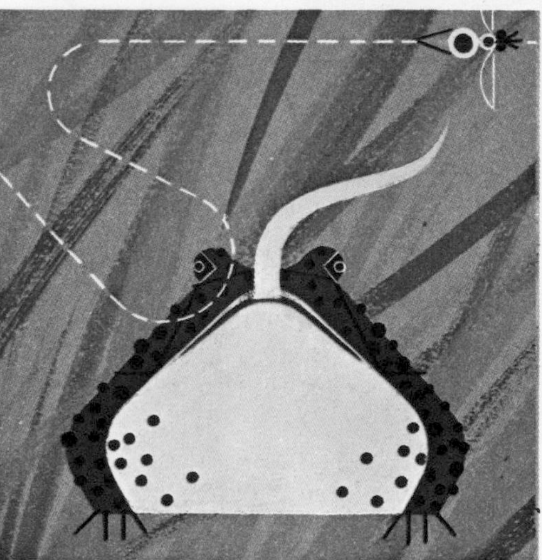

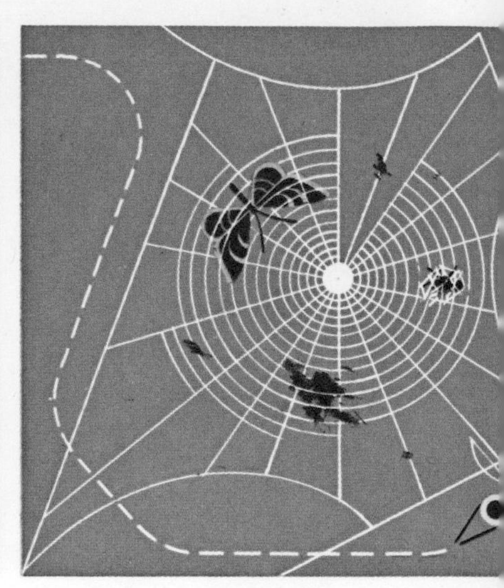

A bee fly eludes a bass . . . *a toad . . .* *a spider's web . . .*

animals, though they perform many amazing feats. Nearly everything an insect does is as automatic as if the animal were a robot. Few insects can change their behavior to suit the circumstance. Individuals do not borrow ideas from each other or improve on their actions as they repeat them.

The most complicated feats of insects are performed by the various nest builders. The individual cells of a honeybee's comb are perfect hexagons. Each is thin-walled yet strong enough to hold its fill of honey. Each is tipped slightly to the rear so the honey has a natural tendency to flow into the cell and exerts the least pressure on the cap over its top. And each cell, in precision row after row, is part of a spatula-shaped hanging comb spaced just the right distance from the combs on either side so that workers can tend both combs without interfering with each other.

The comb is produced and sculptured by young worker bees that have served their time as nurses for the developing brood. Comb building is their last duty before it becomes their turn to go into the field to search for pollen and nectar. These young bees, their stomachs gorged with honey, assemble in a mass and cling one to the other to form a milling curtain hang-

A basilisk rejects some bad-tasting butterflies, probably because of experiences with them in the past. Instead, he grabs a tasty morpho. The butterfly at far left is edible, too, but because it mimics those with a bad taste it escapes.

a shrew . . .

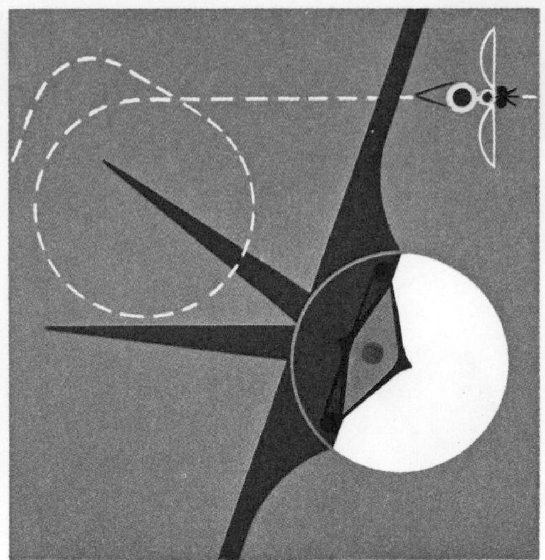

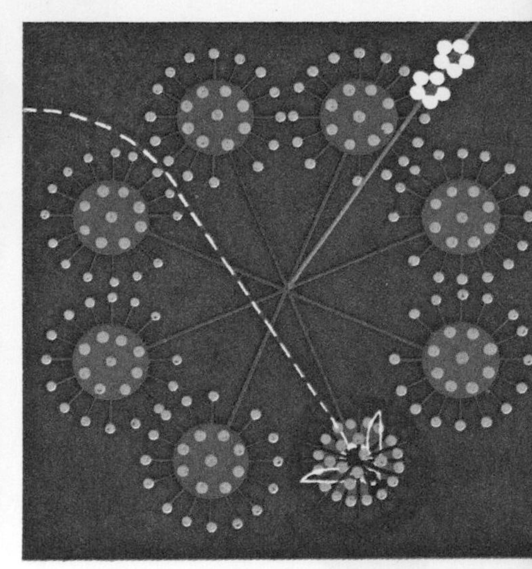

and a swallow, but is caught by a carnivorous sundew plant.

ing from the roof at a spot selected for the comb. Then, from between the segments of the abdomen on the underside of each worker's body, scales of wax begin to appear. Each bee impales a flaky scale on a spur of its hind leg, passes it forward to its mouth and begins chewing. The wax, made sticky by secretions from the bee's mouth, is applied first to the roof to form a foundation for the comb. Then, cell by cell, the bees give the comb its shape.

As the wax is put into place, the bee kneads it with its mandibles, pulling it into a soft, thin sheet and shaping it to fit against the cells on either side. The cell walls are less than one two-hundredths of an inch thick. Every pound of wax, produced from nearly half a million wax scales, is stretched to make more than 30,000 cells in which 20 pounds of honey can be stored. And every pound of wax, in turn, required the consumption of about five pounds of honey by the comb builders.

Honeybees cannot change the architecture of their cells, however. Like all insects, no matter what their particular accomplishments, a honeybee's behavior is largely inherited. It is guided in what it does mostly by instinct, that mysterious inborn force that gives animals a seeming wisdom without thought.

Some protective devices of insects: kallima butterfly (left) looks like dead leaf; puss moth caterpillar lifts head and tail menacingly; bombardier beetle sprays caterpillar hunter beetle with repellent cloud; Io moth surprises a wren with a frightening eye pattern.

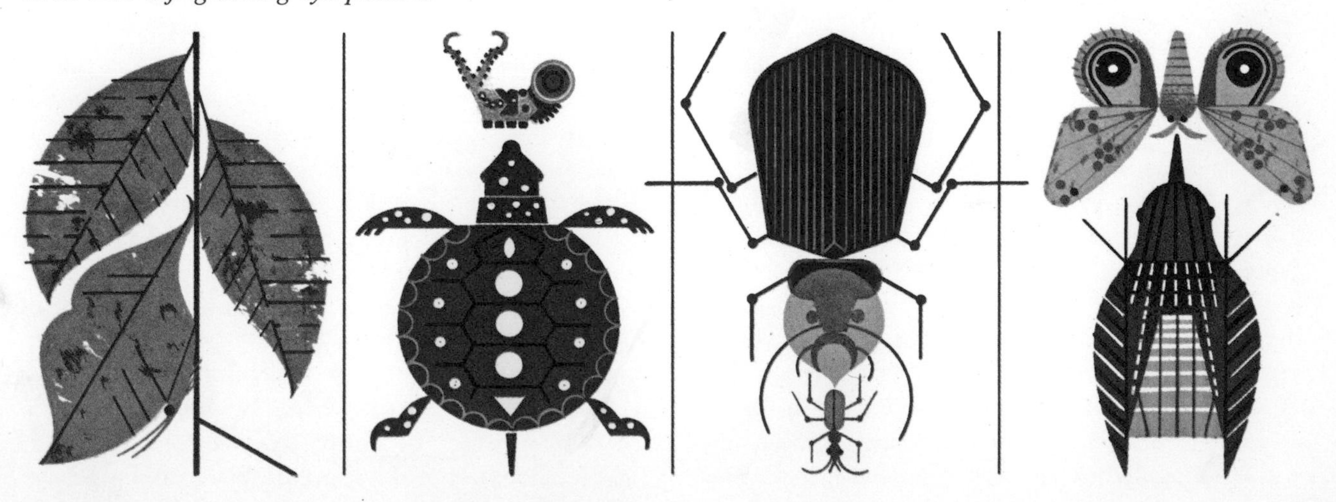

Treehoppers of the tropics have fantastic shapes.

Termites, a much more primitive group of insects, also live in colonies. Large numbers of termites combine their efforts to build a nest, or home, that provides shelter, food, and care for their young. Most of the many species of termites live in subterranean nests, and the workers, which make up the bulk of the colony's population, are blind and soft-bodied. They will die if exposed to the air for only a few hours. The nest is always closed, with only temporary openings made in it at times to let out winged swarmers to start new colonies.

Some of the above-ground termite nests built in the desert and savanna lands of Africa, Australia and South America are 20 feet tall and 50 feet in circumference at their base. They are made of particles of soil cemented together with saliva and excretions and are baked by the sun until they are as hard as concrete. Near the center of the nest are the chambers of the royal couple, the king and queen. Passageways to the queen's royal chamber are large enough for the workers to move through them but are much too small for the giant queen herself to travel them. She is a virtual prisoner in her royal chambers, totally dependent on the workers to bring her food and tend her needs.

The humidity inside a termite nest is always close to 99 percent, even though the air outside is dry. Termites of desert regions get this vital water, so essential to their survival, by digging wells as deep as 125 feet into the desert soil to reach the water table.

Some termite mounds are slim, chimney-like structures that serve principally as ventilators for much larger underground excavations. Others are flat-topped and have a narrow stem, like a mushroom. Some are built around the base of a tree, which becomes the core of the nest, and still others are like mountains, broad at the base and tapered to a narrow peak. The most unusual are the tall, wedge-shaped mounds of the magnetic or compass termites of northern Australia. The thin edges always face north and south; the broad, flat sides always east and west.

Ants show even greater versatility than do either honeybees or termites. When the location of a nest becomes intolerable, they move it to a more suitable spot. Some ants change their nest site with the season. In summer they select a place close to food and one where the nest is warmed by the sun. In winter, they move the nest under a rock or a log, where it is more protected.

As they dig their nest, ants pile up the dirt to form a mound. Some species add sticks, leaves, and other debris to make a heap as much as five feet tall and 10 feet in diameter. Other ants build their nest in decaying wood. Carpenter ants can chisel through solid timbers to hollow out their living quarters. Many species of ants use cavities or hollow stems of plants as homes.

Weaver ants make their nests of leaves sewed

together with silk. A number of workers line up along the edge of a leaf, and their weight bends the leaf downward. When it is close enough to a leaf below, the ants grasp its edge in their mandibles and hang on. They are joined by other workers, who help pull the two leaves together. Then workers appear from the nest, each carrying a larva in its mandibles. At the edge of the leaves, each ant squeezes the larva it is carrying. The larva begins to wriggle, and silk glands near its mouth start to function. The worker ant applies this living thread to one leaf, where the sticky silk becomes attached, then moves the larva to the edge of the other leaf where the silk is attached again. The shuttling is repeated until the leaves are fastened together firmly.

Ants of desert lands have developed a unique method of storing honey to tide them through times when food is scarce. Young workers are selected to become living casks of honey, and as long as they live, they cling to the roof of the storage chamber. They accept honey from workers that return from the field with full crops and feed it back when signalled to do so with strokes of a worker's antennae. Their abdomens become globe shaped and honey yellow.

Harvester ants fill their underground granaries with seeds of grasses. They leave the husks of the seeds in piles outside the nest and store only edible kernels. Fungus-growing ants of South and Central America and extreme southern United States carry bits of leaves to their nests

A bat pursues a luna moth.

and chew them up to make a compost on which to grow a kind of fungus. This is eaten by the adults and also fed to the young. Large colonies of these ants may strip a tree or shrub of all its leaves in one night. Thousands of workers move to the plant in single file. Each cuts a piece of leaf and, holding it like a green parasol over its head, carries it back to the nest. The fungus is so important to the colony's existence that the queen takes some of it with her when she goes on her swarming flight to start a new colony.

A favorite food of some species of ants is a sweet substance, called honeydew, excreted by aphids. When an ant approaches an aphid that does not have a drop of honeydew conveniently waiting for it, the ant tickles the aphid with its antennae. The accommodating aphid lifts its abdomen and a drop of honeydew appears at its tip. If by chance the aphid has gone dry, the ant is likely to slaughter it and use it as a meal of meat. When ants find aphids that will provide them with honeydew, they may defend the aphids from enemies or even erect a protecting wall around them. When winter comes, a small number of aphid eggs may be taken into the ant colony where they are kept until spring. Then the newly hatched aphids are returned outdoors, thus giving the colony an early start.

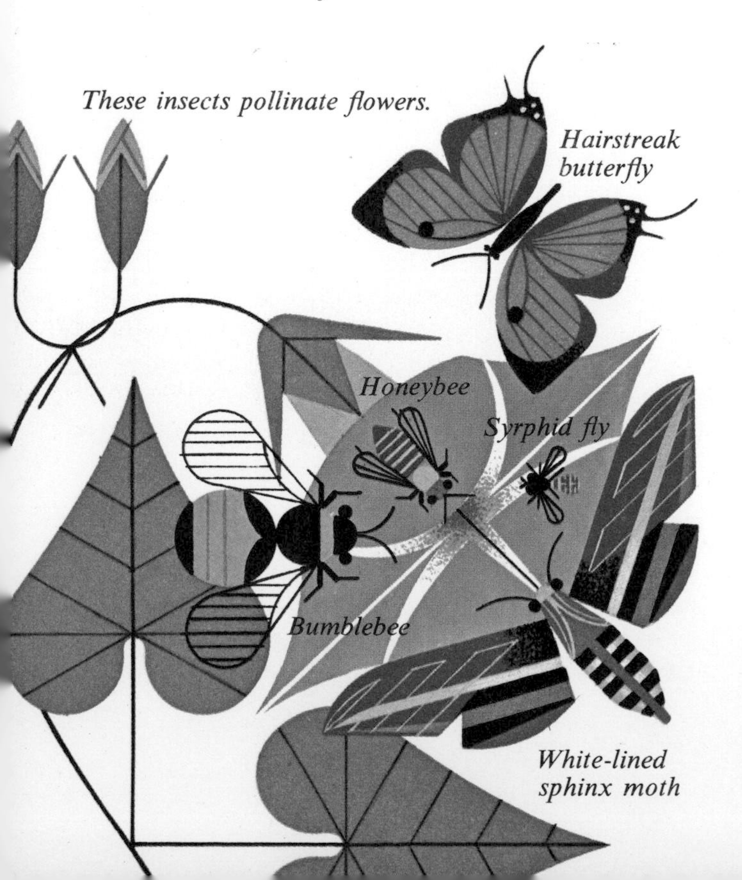

These insects pollinate flowers.

Sharks and Rays

No creatures of the sea are more feared than sharks—and for good reason. A large, hungry shark can make a meal of a man, and such gruesome tales have been front-page news stories with alarming frequency in recent years. In behalf of the sharks, the sea is their world; man is the intruder.

Top villain is the great white shark, or maneater. Though it appears most regularly off the coast of Australia, this sinister giant cruises cool to warm seas throughout the world. It averages 10 to 12 feet long, but is known to exceed 35 feet. It may weigh more than a ton. Sea lions, seals, turtles—anything that moves may be attacked. Even small fishing boats may become the battered, scarred target of a great white shark on the rampage.

Tiger sharks of tropical and subtropical seas are smaller but have probably caused more human deaths than any other sharks. Tiger sharks often come into shallow water to feed on carrion and garbage. If annoyed or attracted to the flashing metal on fishing gear or to the blood from speared fish, they attack fearlessly. The bloody find of one shark commonly attracts a pack of companions.

Shark bite records show that most attacks occur in daylight and in water hip deep or less. These records simply reveal where and when sharks and people are most likely to meet. Actually most sharks feed at night, but when hungry, they will continue their search until they find food. A prowling shark may even invade a crowded bathing beach. When a shark bites, it rolls its body, tearing out chunks of its victim. And while sharks are pictured as having an uncanny, unerring sense for finding living prey, they are not always discriminating. Tin cans, anchors, bottles, automobile tires, concrete blocks, and other quite obviously indigestible items are found in sharks' stomachs.

One of the most dangerous sharks of African and Australian waters is the gray nurse shark. Its close relative in American waters is the sand shark, considered harmless. But like all sharks, the sand shark deserves respect, as there is no sure way of knowing when a shark may change from a sluggish, inoffensive scavenger to a bloodthirsty beast. Even the little dogfish can be formidable. When caught and taken from the water, a dogfish coils its body tightly and then releases suddenly like a spring, driving the sharp, poisonous spine on its dorsal fin into anything in its path. A dogfish let loose in the bottom of a boat can be quite dangerous.

The eyes of the bizarre hammerhead are at the tips of hammer-like extensions at the sides of its head. The diet that appears to delight hammerheads most is sting rays. Commonly a hammerhead's jaws are studded with the sharp spines of rays that battled to keep from becoming its fare. Equally odd is the thresher shark, the sickle-shaped top lobe of its tail fin often as long as the shark's body. Threshers use this giant tail fin to herd fish into tight schools, then swim through the school with mouth open to engulf their prey.

A whale shark, largest of all fish.

Largest of the sharks is the great whale shark, which may exceed a length of 40 feet and a weight of 10 tons. Despite its gargantuan size, the whale shark is harmless. It feeds on tiny animals strained from the sea.

Most of the some 300 kinds of sharks have a torpedo-shaped body and are swift swimmers. The mako shark has been clocked at more than 40 miles per hour.

Rays, of the same group of fishes as sharks, are flat-bodied, and most of them live on or near the bottom of the sea. Their broad pectoral fins are winglike. Those of the great manta ray, or devilfish, may measure 20 feet across. Mantas, which may weigh a ton and a half, live near the surface in the open sea. Commonly they leap from the water, crashing back with a resounding smack. Hornlike fins at each side of the mouth form a scoop that funnels small fish and other animals into the manta's mouth as it swims.

Some rays feed on oysters and other shellfish, crushing the shells with their stout, flat teeth. Many rays have spiny stingers in their tail, which they lash like a whip when disturbed. Torpedo rays can generate as much as 200 volts, used in defense or to stun prey. The charge is powerful enough to knock down a man.

Sawfish have a broad, flat snout, with short, sharp teeth along each margin. They wield this like a club as they swim through schools of fish. Some of the fish are speared, then later scraped off and eaten. Others are stunned or wounded, making them easy to capture.

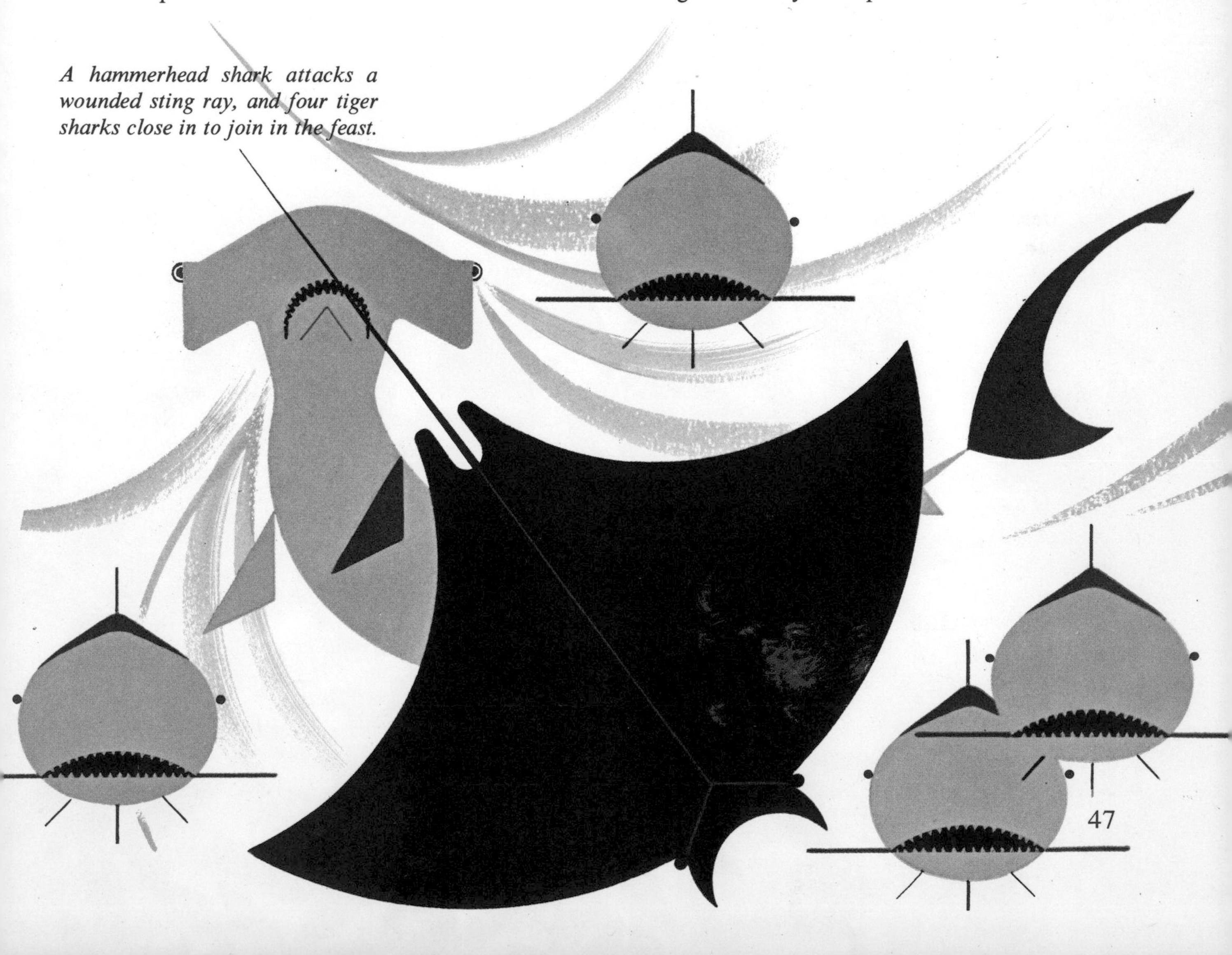

A hammerhead shark attacks a wounded sting ray, and four tiger sharks close in to join in the feast.

Bony Fishes

Tiny goby fishes that live in mountain streams in the Philippines are the smallest animals with backbones. They measure less than half an inch long, and it takes thousands of them to weigh a pound.

Giants among the bony fishes are ocean sunfish, or mola molas, that reportedly weigh as much as a ton. Tunas, swordfish, halibuts, and several other kinds of salt-water fish may weigh more than half a ton. But by far the majority of the more than 40,000 species of bony fishes —the most numerous in kinds and numbers of all animals with backbones—are less than three feet long and weigh less than five pounds. Skeletons of bone distinguish these fishes from sharks and rays, which have skeletons of gristle, or cartilage.

Bony fishes are found in all waters of the world, from booming surfs to quiet five-mile deeps of the seas, and from rushing mountain streams to stagnant ponds. Some live in the eternal blackness of cave waters and are blind. Others thrive in hot springs.

Toothless fresh-water suckers get their food from bottom muds. Other fishes strain small plants and animals from the currents of water drawn over their gills. Parrotfishes have powerful, sharp beaks with which they bite off chunks of coral to get at the soft parts of the animal inside. Archer fish spit pellets of water at spiders and insects above the surface, knocking them into the water where they can be grabbed and eaten.

Most bloodthirsty of the fishes—and possibly of all animals alive—are the 10-inch South American piranhas, or cannibal fish. Schools of these savages will attack any animals that venture into the streams where they live. With their razor-sharp teeth and ravenous appetites, piranhas can reduce an animal the size of a cow to a fleshless skeleton within minutes. Fish use their teeth to hold and to tear apart food. They do not chew.

Many fish that live in the deep sea have glowing lights along the sides of their body and on the tips of rodlike filaments of their fins. These lights attract smaller animals on which the deep-sea fishes feed. Or some flash on their lights suddenly in the darkness, either blinding or scaring away attackers. These strange, deep-sea fish are all small, most of them less than a foot long. All are meat eaters, and because food is scarce and hard to catch in their vast black world, they are equipped to take advantage of every opportunity that chances their way. With their numerous needle-sharp teeth they can hold a catch no matter how hard it struggles. Their mouth and stomach are so large that some can swallow fish larger than themselves.

Variations in shape, size, and color seem endless in the fish world. Warm seas contain the most different kinds of fishes, and nowhere does the colorful array compare to that of a coral reef. But the largest numbers of a single kind of fish are in cold seas. Gigantic schools of herrings, the most plentiful of all fish, contain literally billions of individuals. Each kind of fish is limited to a particular type of water. All trout, for example, live in cold water, some kinds in fast streams and others in the deep, cold lakes. Fresh-water sunfish, in contrast, are found most abundantly in warm streams, lakes, and ponds.

Fishes breathe by taking water in through their mouth and passing it out over their gills. In the process, carbon dioxide is released from the blood, and oxygen is absorbed.

Nearly all fishes are covered with thin, overlapping scales over which there is a protective coating of slime. Growth rings on their scales are much like the annual rings in the trunk of a tree and can be counted to learn a fish's age. Width of the rings may also reveal the years of rapid growth or of slow growth as determined by the abundance and availability of food.

Fast swimmers have a spindle-shaped or streamlined body; those that live and feed close to the bottom have a flat body. By varying the amount of gas in their air bladder, fishes adjust to various levels in the water to find food or to locate the most suitable water temperature. The lateral lines along the sides of a fish's body de-

A school of piranhas attack a cow crossing a stream and reduce her to a skeleton in seconds.

tect vibrations or the direction of flow of water currents.

Fishes that lay many eggs, as do salt-water cods or fresh-water carp, do not protect either the eggs or the young. Few of the young survive. Fishes that lay fewer eggs may build nests and guard the eggs, and some kinds continue to protect the young for a while after the eggs hatch. Male sea catfish pick up the eggs as the female lays them and carry them in their mouth until they hatch. And the young continue to use the male's mouth as a hiding place for several weeks after hatching. The female of a South American catfish carries her eggs in soft tissues on her belly. The tissues form a pocket around each egg. Still other fishes carry their eggs inside their body until they hatch and then "give birth" to the young. Male seahorses have a belly pouch in which they carry the eggs laid by the female, and when the eggs hatch, the young continue to use the pouch as a place to hide.

Coelacanths, the most primitive of living fishes, are members of a group once believed to have been extinct for about 60 million years. Then, in 1938, commercial fishermen netted a coelacanth in deep water near the Comoro Islands off the coast of South Africa. More coelacanths caught in the years since have given scientists an opportunity to study these living fossils, for it is believed that ancient fringed and lobe-finned fishes of this group gave rise to modern fishes and to all other animals with backbones.

The nearest living relatives of coelacanths are the lungfishes that live in fresh-water streams and ponds in Africa and Australia. A lungfish's air bladder is supplied with many blood vessels and serves as a lung. The fish rises to the surface from time to time to take in gulps of air. During the dry season in the tropics, the ponds and streams in which lungfishes live dry up, and the fish burrow into the mud at the bottom. These mud casings become baked hard across the top by the sun but are connected to the surface by a small air hole. Inside these mud cocoons, the lungfish remains curled and motionless, or dormant. When the rains come again, the

Some Fish Profiles

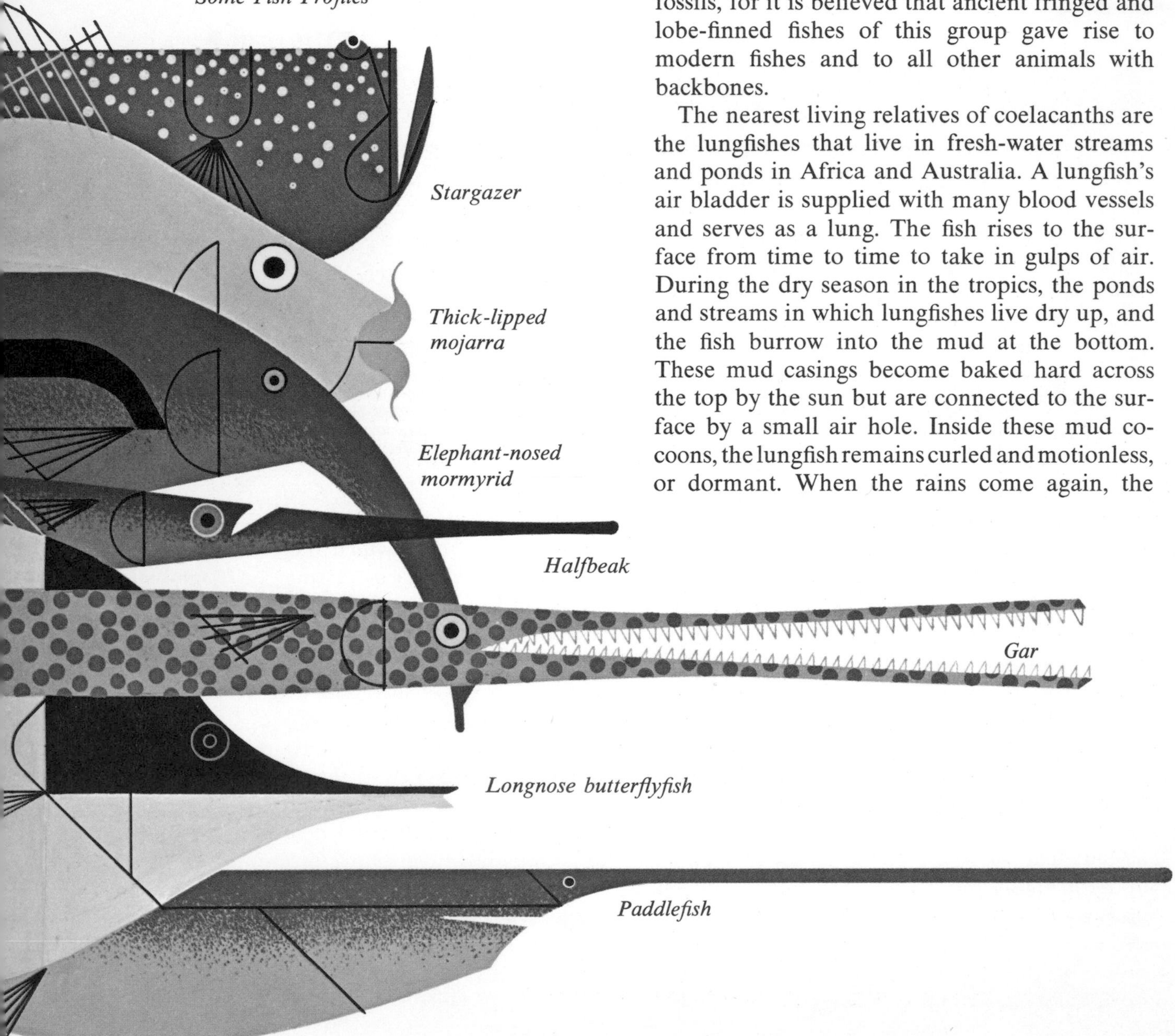

Stargazer

Thick-lipped mojarra

Elephant-nosed mormyrid

Halfbeak

Gar

Longnose butterflyfish

Paddlefish

Sockeye salmon leaping waterfalls on their way upstream to spawn (left).

Young seahorses hatch from eggs carried in belly pouch of male (right).

pool fills with water and the mud softens. Then the lungfish wriggles out and resumes normal living. A lungfish may stay alive in its mud casing for three or four years without taking in either food or water.

Sturgeons and paddlefish, largest of the fresh-water fishes, resemble sharks. They have more cartilage in their skeleton than do other bony fishes. At the tip of a sturgeon's shovel-shaped snout are four long whiskers that drag along the bottom as the fish swims. These serve as taste feelers for finding food. When a morsel of food is found, the sturgeon sticks out its tubelike mouth, located behind the whiskers, and sucks in the morsel. A paddlefish's long, spatula-shaped snout is a sensitive organ used to locate the tiny microscopic plants and animals (plankton) that it eats. Paddlefish have a leathery skin and only a few scales; sturgeons are covered with bony plates. Sturgeon eggs are eaten as caviar. The roe of a large female sturgeon may weigh as much as 300 pounds and contain more than a million eggs. Large sturgeons may weigh more than 1,000 pounds.

A few kinds of fish can survive in water that lacks sufficient oxygen for most kinds of life. Fresh-water gars and bowfins live in warm, stagnant waters. They come to the surface from time to time to replenish their air supply. The carp and many kinds of catfish can survive in water in which the oxygen content is low. If they are kept moist and cool, they can remain alive out of water for many hours. Mudskippers of tropical southeastern Asia hop about on the mud flats. Climbing perch bask on the roots of trees growing in or near the water.

Plä buks, of Thailand, and wels, of the Danube and other European rivers, may weigh about 500 pounds. They are the largest members of the catfish family. The catfish of North America range in size from the 100-pounders of the Mississippi to tiny madtoms that live in swift

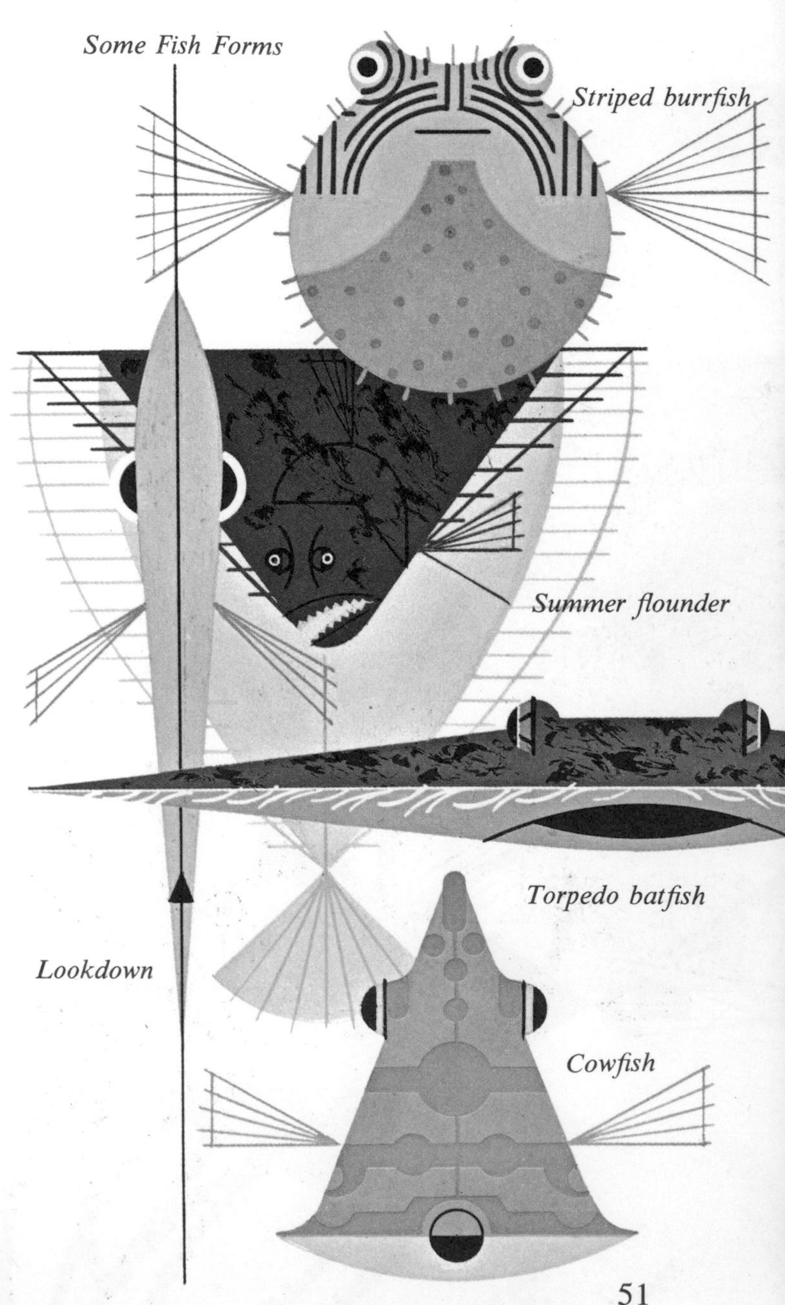

streams. Most abundant are the several kinds of bullheads.

Most catfish lack scales and have a slick, slimy skin, but some kinds are covered with armored plates. Nearly all catfish have long, catlike whiskers that are sensory organs used to find food by its taste or odor. In many species the taste organs are scattered over their body so the catfish can literally taste or smell food with its tail. Most catfish have sharp spines in their fins with which the fish can give a painful stab wound that is slow to heal. Electric catfish of the Nile and other rivers of North Africa can produce a jolting charge of electricity used mainly as a defense weapon. A tiny South American catfish lives in the gill cavities of larger fish, chewing on its gill filaments and feeding on the blood that oozes out. Another unusual South American catfish always swims upside down.

Slim and snakelike eels are bony fishes that live in both fresh and salt water. An electric eel about three feet long can produce more than 600 volts, the greatest amount of voltage generated by any fish. Morays are eels of warm seas, especially abundant around coral reefs. Some of the more than 40 species of moray eels reach a length of 10 feet. They commonly attack and bite with little provocation. They have a powerful bite and tear the flesh with their sharp, recurved teeth. But a moray's bite is not poisonous.

The most familiar of the eels are those that live in fresh water. After living a number of years in fresh water, the adult eels travel to the sea and swim to an area near the Sargasso Sea where they spawn and then die. The baby eels that hatch from the eggs laid in the sea do not resemble the adults, but they change in appearance as they journey from their place of hatching to coastal streams. Those that travel to America complete their 1,000-mile journey in about a year. Those that travel to Europe swim nearly 3,000 miles, and their trip takes three years.

In contrast to the journey of the eels to the

Queen triggerfish escapes a predator by diving into a sea whip.

(1) An archer fish downs an ant with water pellets.
(2) A foraging tern scatters a school of anchovies.

sea to spawn, salmons travel from the sea up fresh-water streams to lay their eggs. Some of the Pacific salmons journey more than 2,000 miles inland to their spawning grounds in headwaters of rivers. Special "fish ladders" are built to assist them in getting around or over dams built in their path, or they may be guided to new spawning areas by odor trails. Pacific salmon die after spawning, but the salmons of the Atlantic may return to the sea.

Some fishes spend their lives very near or at the surface of the water. One of the most remarkable is the four-eyed fish of Mexico and Central America. Its eyes are bulges on the top of its head, and the lens is egg-shaped so that the fish can see both above and below the surface. Flying fishes, most of them less than a foot long, are one of the thrilling sights to be seen at sea. Whole schools may suddenly appear above the surface and glide for hundreds of yards above the waves, their thin membranous "wings" rattling in the wind. Sometimes they dip low enough so that their tail is in the water, and they vibrate it rapidly to gain momentum to remain airborne. Mosquitofish, or gambusias, are minnows that swim and feed close to the surface. Their mouth points upward, making it easy for them to take their food from the surface. They are one of the important ways of controlling mosquitoes, as they feed on the mosquito "wrigglers" and "tumblers" that live on the water's surface.

Cleaners at work: a striped wrasse, left, obligingly cleans a surgeonfish, while below a bluehead wrasse cleans a red parrotfish. At right, a rainbow wrasse works over a dragon moray eel.

A deep-sea angler uses its light to lure fish.

Fishes are one of the world's major food resources. They are rich in protein and are low in fat content. Some kinds are processed to get oils or to make fish meals and fertilizers. In addition, fish provide sport fishermen many hours of pleasure. In the United States, the more than 40 million sport fishermen every year catch an estimated billion pounds of fish, roughly half from fresh water and half from salt water. While many sport fishermen eat their catch, fishing is most important as a means of relaxing from the tensions of modern living. One scientist called fishing a "dignified way of doing nothing."

This aggressive South American horned frog fearlessly attacks animals many times its size. This brave one is biting a horse.

Amphibians

The fat, blinking toad sitting under the patio light seems unaware of the world about it. But when a June bug rattles to the ground nearby and begins crawling toward the light, the toad leans forward, its nose aimed directly at the unsuspecting insect. Suddenly the crouched, warty amphibian opens its mouth wide and its tongue lashes out, the sticky tip wrapping around the beetle. Just as quickly, the tongue and its hapless victim are withdrawn, and the mouth snaps shut.

The toad's amazing tongue is fastened at the front of its mouth rather than at the rear. This gives the toad full use of the tongue's length to capture prey, and with the free tip at the back of the mouth, the prey is automatically headed toward the toad's stomach. By tightening its head muscles, which may even make the bulging eyes sink into their sockets, the toad squeezes its catch off the tip of its tongue and pushes it downward. When daylight comes, the toad hops into the shadows to retire. All day it stays in hiding in some dark, damp place in the soft dirt in a garden, in sand, or in leaf litter.

Toads, along with frogs, salamanders, and newts—some 2,000 species—are amphibians, the first animals to live on land. Some of the prehistoric amphibians were 15 feet long. All of the ancient amphibians looked like big salamanders; none resembled frogs or toads. The largest today

An eastern newt, left, eats its skin when it molts. Right, a spotted cave salamander looks at tree outside.

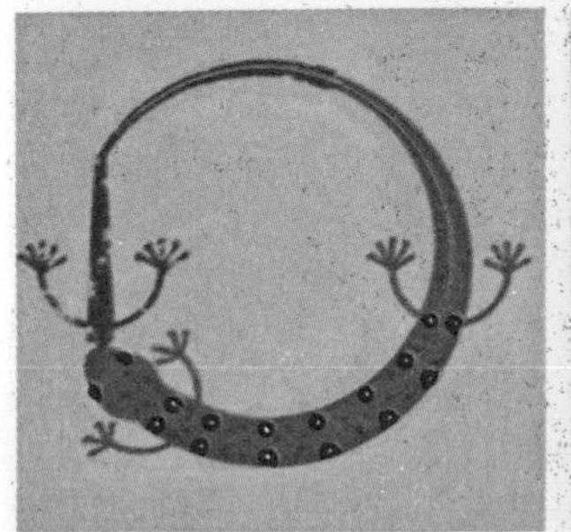

is the five and a half foot, 100-pound giant salamander of Japan. This big salamander lives underwater but comes to the surface from time to time to breathe. The smallest amphibians are tiny Cuban frogs less than half an inch long when full grown. The little female lays only one egg. Nearly as small are the inch-long pygmy salamanders of southeastern United States.

Frogs and toads have strong hind legs and can jump to escape enemies. Some can even jump backwards. In championship frog-jumping contests, held with all the flurry and fanfare of an Olympic event, the winning frogs have jumped over 16 feet in a single leap. They must repeat this distance for three consecutive jumps to have the distance declared official. Though salamanders and newts do not have jumping legs, many use their tail to push themselves in short-distance, sideways jumps. Under attack they may pop off their tail and leave it behind to satisfy the pursuer while they escape.

Typically, a female amphibian lays her eggs in water, where they are fertilized by a male. Toads usually lay their eggs in long strings; frogs and salamanders lay their eggs in clumps or masses. The eggs hatch into larval forms—called tadpoles in the case of frogs and toads—that live in water and breathe with gills. After a period of development, varying from a few weeks to several years depending on the kind of amphibian, the larvae lose their gills, develop lungs, and change into air-breathing adults. The digestive tract also changes, from very long in the plant-eating tadpoles of frogs and toads to very short in the flesh-eating adults. Frog and toad tadpoles lose their tail and legs appear—first the hind legs, then the front. Salamander and newt larvae are carnivorous, like the adults, and the larvae do not lose their tail.

The male midwife toad of southwestern Europe carries the eggs laid by the female on his back until they hatch. The males of a South American frog swallow the eggs laid by the female. The eggs hatch and develop in a pouch inside his body, emerging as fully developed frogs. Eggs of the Surinam toad are pushed into the soft tissues on the female's back by the male.

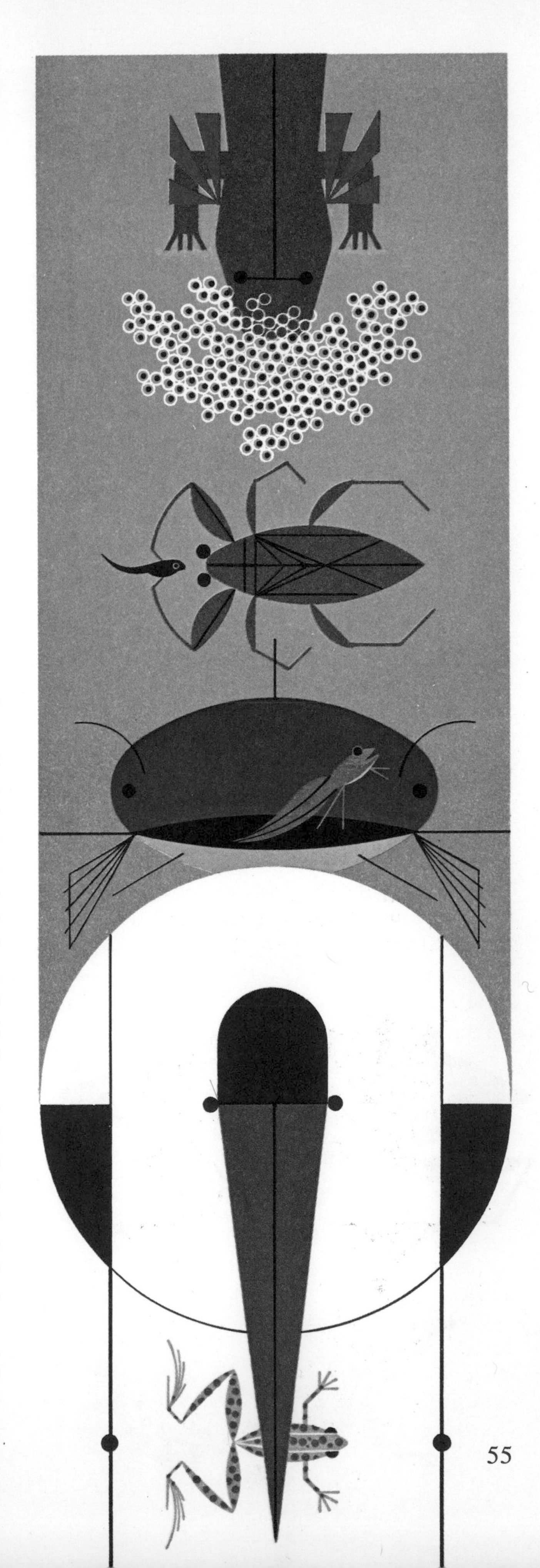

Frogs and their tadpoles make meals for many animals. Leopard frog eggs are eaten by a mudpuppy (top), the tadpoles by a giant waterbug and a catfish (middle), and the adult by a wood ibis.

There each egg sinks into a pocket, capped with a lid of gelatin. Inside these pockets the eggs hatch and the larvae develop into young frogs. Some kinds of frogs and salamanders lay their eggs in damp leaves or in water-filled hollow stems. When they hatch, the larvae hitch a ride on an adult to a pool of water in which they complete their development.

Amphibians are cold-blooded animals. They survive cold winters in temperate climates by hibernation, burying themselves in the mud below the frost line. During this period they absorb the small amount of oxygen they need through their skin and are nourished from the fats stored in their body. Amphibians cannot withstand extremely dry, high temperatures. At these times, too, they become dormant. Amphibians typically have moist skins and must live either in or near water. As a group, they are the intermediate step between the wholly aquatic fish and the land-dwelling reptiles. There are, of course, some amphibians that dwell in deserts and some reptiles that are aquatic, but these are exceptions to the rule.

No amphibians live in salt water, though some are found in brackish-water marshes. They are widely distributed in fresh waters, and are most abundant in the moist tropics. A few kinds are adapted to life in deserts, escaping the heat and dryness by burrowing into the sand. Some are equipped with horny, spadelike feet for digging. They commonly preserve water in their body, which becomes a water-filled sack. Desert dwellers have learned to quench their thirst from these baggy-bodied toads. Some of the burrowers have bony helmets on their head. These helmets also serve as protective doors to their burrows.

A large group of frogs are tree dwellers and can cling to vertical surfaces or even hang upside down using the adhesive suction cups on their toes. Some South American tree frogs do not leave their trees even to lay eggs. The eggs are laid in a liquid secreted with them, and this liquid is whipped into a froth that surrounds

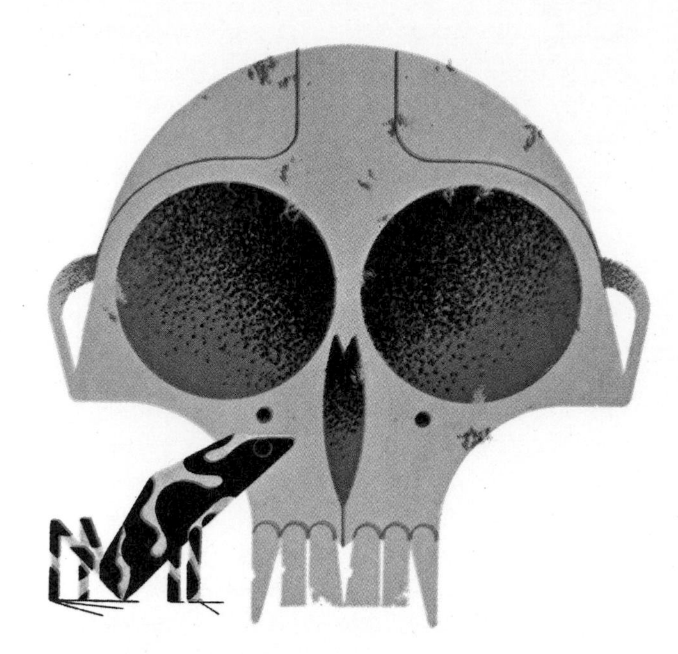

South American Indians tip their arrows with poison made from secretions of the skins of frogs, like this one shown by a capuchin's skull.

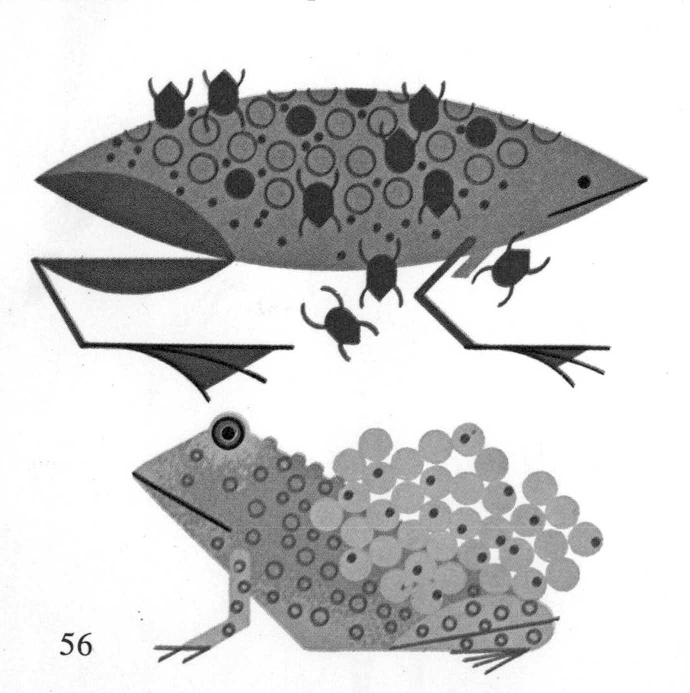

Surinam toads (left) hatch from pits in the skin of a female's back, while the midwife toad (lower left) carries her eggs on her back until they hatch.

A Fowler's toad sings in the moonlight to attract a mate.

and protects the eggs from drying until they hatch. An Asiatic frog has wide webs between its toes on both front and hind legs and can glide from tree to tree or from trees to the ground. Many tree frogs can change their color. The males give shrill, birdlike mating calls in spring. Each species can be identified by its call.

The ability of toads to give off a milky fluid from the warty bumps on their back probably gave rise to the mistaken belief that toads cause warts. The gummy secretion does not cause warts, but it is a foul-tasting, stinging poison that discourages dogs or other animals that might like to make a meal of a toad. The poison of the giant nine-inch marine toad of southeastern United States and the American tropics, and of the nearly as large Colorado river toad is powerful enough to kill dogs and other animals that try to catch or eat these amphibians. The poison secreted by Central and South American arrow-poison frogs is used by the Indians on the tips of their arrows and darts and is strong enough to cause the instant death of sizable animals.

Salamanders and newts have tails, distinguishing them from the tailless toads and frogs. Unlike frogs and toads, these tailed amphibians lack ears and do not make noises, with a few questionable exceptions of salamanders that exhale noisily. Thus they live silently, quite in contrast to the clamoring bedlam frogs make when they are plentiful.

Many salamanders continue to be aquatic and retain their gills throughout their life. Some land-dwelling salamanders do not have lungs. They breathe through their skin and also absorb oxygen through the moist lining of their mouth. Salamanders that live in cave streams are colorless and blind, and one group exists in deep artesian waters, absorbing food and oxygen from the water and never coming to the surface. Most salamanders live on the ground, under rocks, or leaves, but a few species burrow into the ground and others live in trees, especially among the air plants in the rain forests of the tropics.

Congo eels and sirens are slim, eel-like salamanders. Congo eels have four rudimentary legs; sirens have only the front pair. Both Congo eels and sirens may reach a length of three or more feet; they live in the drainage ditches and canals of southeastern United States. Hellbenders and mudpuppies, each about a foot long, are chunky-bodied stream-dwelling salamanders. Both are widely distributed in the United States, but are found mostly in the large rivers in midwestern states. The mudpuppy keeps its gills; the wrinkly-skinned hellbender loses its gills, but the gill slits remain.

A flying frog (left) leaps from a leafy branch. Pickerel frog (right) nabs a sulfur butterfly.

Most primitive of the amphibians are the blind, legless, and wormlike caecilians of the tropics. Some kinds are slim and nearly four feet long; others are short and thick-bodied. Like other amphibians, the caecilians feed on insects, worms, and similar small animals.

Snakes

A jaguar, most water-loving of all the cats, pads stealthily beneath a tree on the bank of a broad river in the tropics. Warily the cat studies the broad expanse of water, perhaps sensing danger. Suddenly a great writhing weight crashes down from the branches of the tree, and the cat is caught in the viselike crushing coils of an anaconda, or water boa.

Unquestionably the heaviest of all snakes, a large anaconda may weigh nearly 500 pounds. It is possibly also the largest of all snakes, as tales are told of anacondas more than 40 feet long. The longest official record is 30 feet. Unlike other boas, the anaconda is almost always found near water. Most members of the boa family are less than five feet long, and even the famous boa constrictor rarely exceeds a length of 10 feet.

Boas are exceeded in size as a group only by the pythons, the largest of which is the Asiatic reticulated python. There is an authentic record of a reticulated python 33 feet long, and records of several African rock pythons nearly as long. No python is a match for the anaconda in bulk, however. Unique among snakes, the female Indian python incubates her eggs, the temperature of her body actually rising as she lies coiled about the eggs until they hatch.

Snakes are probably the most talked about of all animals, but much that is said is not complimentary and a good bit of it is more myth than fact. The story of the wicked serpent in the Garden of Eden and similar legends of other peoples have made the snake a symbol of sin. Because its eyes are lidless, a snake has an unblinking stare, but it is not able to hypnotize its prey.

An anaconda catches a jaguar.

The common belief that snakes are slimy is not so. They are dry and scaly. Periodically they shed the thin layer of skin covering the scales, first rubbing it loose at the nose and then crawling out. The frequency of shedding depends on how rapidly the snake is growing and how well fed it is. Snakes are feared, too, because some kinds are poisonous. And though most snakes are harmless, it is nevertheless true that no other group of animals has a higher percentage of poisonous kinds among its members.

In drop for drop of venom, the most poisonous snake in the world is said to be the tiger snake of Australia, where three-fourths of all the kinds of snakes are venomous. But the tiger snake does not cause the most deaths. This questionable distinction goes to Russell's viper of Asia. Russell's viper is not only easily provoked to bite but also lives in more heavily populated areas than does the tiger snake.

Largest of the poisonous snakes is the notorious king cobra, averaging 12 feet in length and known to reach 18 feet. The king cobra, which feeds almost exclusively on other snakes, is not normally aggressive. The female lays her eggs in a crude nest of debris pushed together and then guards the nest until the eggs hatch. During this time she will attack any intruder.

By lifting long, hinged ribs, a cobra can spread the loose skin on its neck thus forming a hood. The most magnificent is the spectacle-marked hood of the Indian cobra. Snake charmers perform their fascinating dangerous show by tapping on the basket containing the cobra to disturb the snake and make it rise. Then the snake matches the movements of the charmer in a swaying dance that is climaxed when the snake charmer kisses the deadly cobra. Usually the snake does not have its fangs pulled, and the charmer must be skilled or he loses his life. Snake charmers usually play music on a pipe, but as the snakes are deaf, it is the movement of the snake charmer's body that "charms" the snake.

Kraits, smaller relatives of cobras, are abundant in Southeast Asia. They are probably responsible for more of the 25,000 deaths due to snakebite in India than are cobras. Most spectacular of the cobra clan are those that can spit their venom, best developed in African snakes. They aim for their victim's eyes; at about 10 feet they

A black mamba escaping a brush fire has been caught by a patrolling secretary bird.

are deadly accurate. A direct hit will cause blindness. The openings in the fangs of spitting cobras are directed forward rather than down as they are in those that inject the venom into their bites. The most feared of all African snakes are the slim, speedy mambas because of their vicious dispositions. The most famous historically is the asp, or Egyptian cobra, used by Cleopatra to commit suicide.

Cobra venom affects the nerves, death usually resulting from suffocation when the breathing mechanism is paralyzed. Sea snakes, found abundantly in the Pacific and Indian oceans, also have a neurotoxic venom. The seas may at times swarm with literally millions of these highly poisonous snakes, some of them eight feet long, but they rarely attack humans.

Coral snakes, widely distributed throughout the world, are also cobra relatives. Two kinds live in the United States. They are shy, colorful snakes that seldom cause deaths because they are not easily provoked to bite. Even when they do bite, they have difficulty injecting venom. Coral snakes of the United States are attractively ringed with red, black, and yellow. Harmless snakes that look like coral snakes never have the red bands bordered with yellow.

Vipers are poisonous snakes with well-developed hollow fangs which inject venom into the bite wound like hypodermic needles. The fangs of the colorfully insidious gaboon viper of Africa are nearly two inches long. The cottonmouth, copperhead, and some 15 species of rattlesnakes are vipers native to the United States. The diamondback rattlesnake of Florida is the largest snake in the United States. It may grow to a length of eight feet. Poisonous snakes, however, cause fewer deaths in the United States than do the stings of insects and the bites of spiders.

The only poisonous snake of Europe is a viper, distinctive also because it ranges north of the

Arctic Circle. The European viper gives birth to its young, which develop in the female for two years before being born.

Pit vipers have a tiny pit between each eye and the nostril. With these special sensory organs the snake can detect such slight differences in heat that it can determine whether a rat is in a burrow without having to explore the burrow's full length. Largest and most vicious of the pit vipers is the bushmaster of the American tropics. About eight feet long, the bushmaster is quick to attack. An equally nervous, mean-dispositioned snake is the tropical American fer-de-lance, known also as the barba amarilla because of the bright yellow under its chin.

Poisonous snakes use their venom to kill their prey. Many snakes that lack potent venom nevertheless have a slightly poisonous saliva that helps to stop the struggles of their victims. Other snakes either kill their prey by suffocating it in crushing, constricting coils or hold it down with loops of the body as they swallow it—always head first and whole.

One of the most remarkable features of a snake is its elastic lower jaw. The two halves of the lower jawbone can be spread wide by means of a stretchable ligament, and the jawbones also

A bird-hunting rhinoceros viper has finished a meal.

On a rough branch, a corn snake pulls off its old skin and emerges with bright colors.

become disjointed at the rear. This permits the snake to swallow animals that are much bulkier than itself. And if the animal is still alive and squirming, it is held in place by the snake's teeth that curve backward, allowing movement in only one direction—down into the snakes's stomach.

Short, fat-bodied hognosed snakes, common in the United States, are completely harmless. When it is first encountered, a hognosed snake raises the front of its body, hisses loudly and flattens its neck, much as a cobra does. It makes mock strikes but never really opens its mouth. If the intruder does not leave, the snake next flops onto its back and writhes and twists as though dying a violent death. Finally it becomes quiet, its mouth open and its tongue lolled out. If it is turned onto its stomach, it flips quickly onto its back again, insisting that a dead snakes lies belly up.

Lizards

On Komodo and nearby islands off the southeastern coast of Asia there lives a real dragon. The largest of all lizards, it may weigh 350 pounds and measure 10 feet long. Flicking its forked, snakelike tongue to test its surroundings, the Komodo dragon prowls the islands in search of prey. Commonly it makes a meal of animals as large as deer or hogs, which it first kills and then tears into chunks. Ordinarily the scaly giant is wary and unapproachable, but when cornered, it wields its tail as a club and becomes as ferocious as it appears. In captivity, Komodo dragons become quite tame.

Like snakes, lizards thrive in warm regions. Those that live in temperate climates survive the cold winters by hibernation. But there are a few more kinds of lizards—about 2,800 species of lizards compared to 2,700 species of snakes—and they are a much more varied group. Lizards are also more common in hot, dry deserts than are snakes. Some of the desert dwellers are so squat that they do not even cast a shadow. They can squirm into the sand to hide or to escape the direct rays of the sun. Others have fringes on their toes and can scamper across the loose sand without sinking in. They are said to be able to run at speeds exceeding 15 miles an hour.

The most obvious difference between lizards and snakes is that lizards have legs. But the so-called "glass snakes" are really legless lizards, and there are other burrowing, legless lizards that have ringed bodies and resemble earthworms both in appearance and habits. Lizards have movable eyelids and external ear openings, which snakes lack. Also they do not have an elastic ligament joining the two halves of the lower jaw as snakes do. Nearly all lizards lay eggs, though a few kinds that live in cold climates give birth to their young.

Only the stubby-tailed gila monsters of southwestern United States and Mexico are poisonous. Their venom is highly potent, affecting the nervous system. Deaths from the bites are rare because gila monsters are not aggressive and do

Komodo dragons fight over a pig.

not have well-developed fangs for injecting their venom. All lizards have strong jaws, however, and can bite.

If a lizard loses its tail, a new one grows to replace it. The new tail is seldom as long as the original and lacks the supporting bony extension of the backbone. When grabbed, the lizard simply pops off its tail, and while the tail continues to wiggle, the lizard dashes off to safety. Some species of lizards—the monitors, for example—cannot shed their tail. If their tail is cut off, it remains short. Others grab their tail in their mouth and thus form such a stiff ring that a predator cannot find a convenient place to hold onto them.

A lizard's tail may be valuable in many ways. To swift runners, many of which run on their hind legs, the long, slim tail serves as a balancer. Those few lizards that enter water use their tail for swimming. Chuckwallas, gila monsters, and many other kinds of lizards have thick-bodied tails in which food reserves are stored. When food is plentiful, the tail becomes fat. If food is scarce, the stored food is used, and the tail slims down. The brightly colored tails of other lizards are waved menacingly at intruders and detracts them from the more vital parts of the lizard's body.

Some of the monitor lizards along the Nile are nearly as large as the Komodo dragon. None of these present-day lizards can compare to the sea-going mosasaurs that lived some 60 million years ago. Some mosasaurs were 20 feet long, with paddle-like legs for swimming. Some had sharp teeth for capturing fish; in others, the teeth were flattened for cracking shells of mollusks grabbed from the bottom. Quite in contrast to these giants are tiny eight-inch monitor lizards of Australia.

Among the more famous of all lizards are the iguanas that live on the rocky Galapagos Islands off the western coast of South America. One kind lives along the seashore and dives into the water to forage on seaweeds; it can swim or walk along the bottom. Using its long, flat tail, it can swim well and is sometimes seen far at sea. The marine

Frilled head of a Galapagos marine iguana.

(1) With its long, sticky tongue, a horned chameleon captures a grasshopper.

(2) A gila monster holds a skunk's heel with a bulldog grip, working poison into wound.

Defensive devices of lizards: (1) a chuckwalla inflates body to stay in rocky niche as a roadrunner tugs on its tail; (2) a flying lizard of Southeast Asia; (3) Delaland's lacertid holds its foot in its mouth to avoid being swallowed by a sand snake; (4) a frilled lizard expands its collar suddenly, startling a predator; (5) a young five-lined skink leaves its tail in an opossum's mouth and scurries away.

iguana may reach a length of about six feet and weigh as much as 25 or 30 pounds. The slightly smaller land iguana lives in the dry interior of the islands. There it feeds on the spiny leaves and the fruits of cactus plants, from which it also gets the moisture it needs.

Chuckwallas are among the several kinds of smaller iguanas found in southwestern United States. A chuckwalla can inflate its body like a balloon and uses this method to wedge itself in rocky crevices to escape predators. Indians, who relished the flesh of the chuckwalla, poked pointed sticks into the lizards to let out the air so they could be pulled from their hiding place. Chuckwallas spend their nights among the rocks to avoid the cold of the desert night, and they do not emerge until the sun has again warmed the rocks and the air above.

Geckos of about 300 species live in the tropics and subtropics. They are mostly small, stubby-bodied lizards with a short, rather thick tail. Nearly all geckos have adhesive pads on their toes making it possible for them to scamper over ceilings. In the tropics, geckos commonly enter houses where they are seen scampering about in search of insects. Most lizards are voiceless, but geckos chirp, croak, and growl, sometimes so loudly that they become annoying when in a house. Like many other kinds of lizards, geckos can shed their tail and grow a new one, but sometimes the old tail hangs on and heals. A new tail grows from the scarred stub anyhow, and the result is a lizard that has two tails.

One of the most bizarre of all lizards is the flying dragon of southeastern Asia. About eight inches long, the flying dragon has flaps of skin along each side of its head and body. When the lizard is resting, the skin hangs in loose folds, but when the lizard goes into action, it lifts its long ribs making a framework over which the flaps of thin skin stretch tightly. With these gliding membranes the lizard can soar from one tree to another, either to escape enemies or to search for insects. It cannot, of course, use these gliding membranes like wings for true flight.

Anoles, or American chameleons, are common in Florida and southward into the Caribbean. Slim and seldom more than six inches long, anoles can change their color from green to brown or vice versa, depending on their background. Courting or fighting males fan out a flap of colorful skin on their throat. In hunting, they move slowly until near their prey, then dart swiftly to make their catch. All of the more than 150 species of anoles of the American subtropics and tropics have a flat, almost triangular head.

If food is hard to find, a green day gecko will eat its own tail.

Spiny swifts of the southern pine woods and the fleet, long-tailed utas of the Southwest are members of the iguana lizard group. So are the desert-dwelling horned lizards (toads), which have a broad, flat, spiny body, a very short tail, and the unusual ability to squirt drops of blood from their eyes when molested. When disturbed, a horned lizard will puff up its body, hiss, assume a defensive position, and then actually attack. Since it can do nothing but pinch, no damage is done. But if this little beast were the size of a dinosaur, this would indeed be a monster to be feared. Even if it were as big as a dog, the story would be quite different.

True chameleons, found mostly in Africa, are chunky lizards with their eyes set in turret-like bulges. Each eye can be moved independently of the other. A chameleon's tail is a grasping organ, as useful in climbing as is a monkey's tail. The long, sticky-tipped tongue can be flicked out and in faster than the human eye can follow the movement. Despite all these peculiarities, the chameleons are known best for their ability to change their color—from gray to green and back again. This they may do to match their background or as an indication of their feeling after males battle with another male. Some male chameleons have crests, horns, or warty bumps on their head. Some have only a single horn, others have two, three, or even four horns. These make the lizards look like quite fearsome warriors, but there is no evidence that the chameleons use these horns in fights. They do more bluffing than battling.

Two male bloodsucker lizards change their colors in the heat of battle.

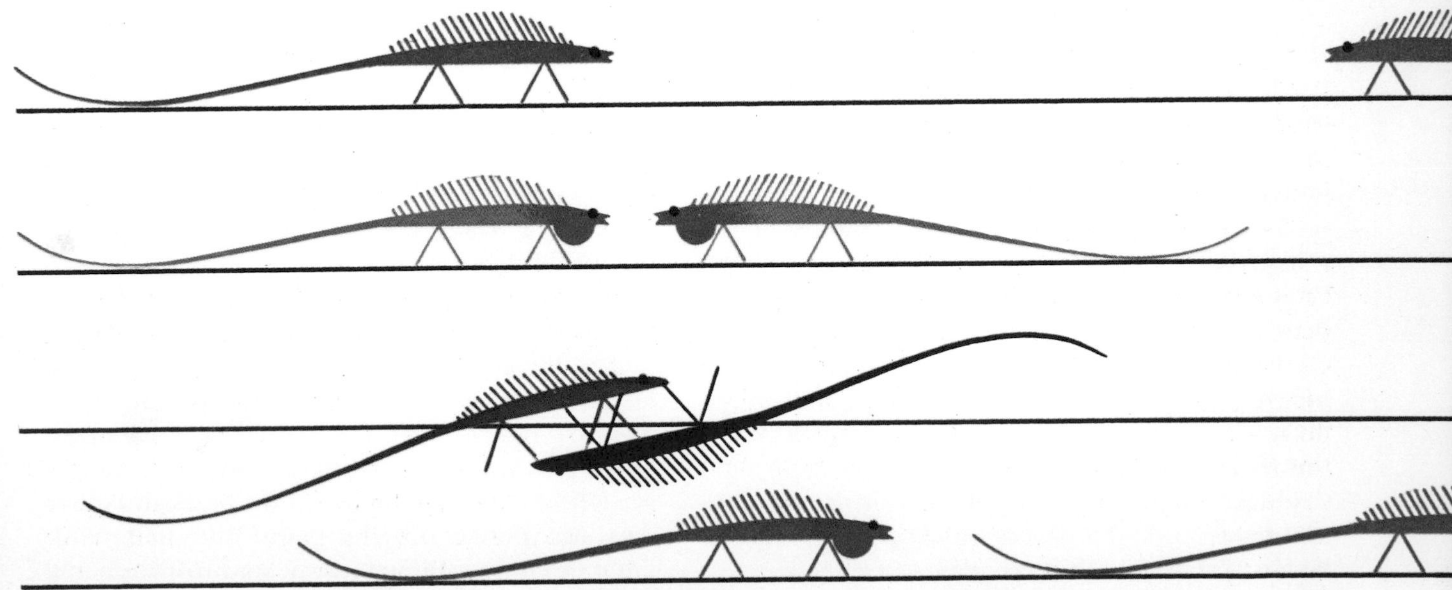

A giant leatherback, most sea-going of the turtles, returns to shore to lay eggs.

Turtles

Turtles beget more turtles by laying eggs. Fresh-water musk turtles, or stinkpots, lay fewer than half a dozen eggs, and either drop them directly on the ground or scoop out a very shallow nest. But for most turtles, egg-laying is a carefully performed annual ritual. For sea turtles, it is the only bond they still have with the land. Even the giant leatherback, the largest and most sea-going of all turtles comes to shore to lay its eggs.

When spring tides are at their peak, female sea turtles come in from the open sea to lay their eggs on sandy beaches. The journey up the beach is extremely difficult, for unable to walk on land, the female must literally heave her ponderous body across the beach. Sometimes she makes several trips from sea to shore before finding a suitable place. It must be sandy so the digging is easy and far enough from the sea so that the eggs do not become soaked in salt water, which will coagulate the yolks.

Digging slowly and laboriously with her flippers, the female pushes away the sand to make a shallow basin in which she settles her body. Directly beneath her, she digs an even deeper hole in which she then lays her eggs—about 150 of them, round, rubbery, and white. And when she is done, the female shoves sand into the hole until it is filled. Then slowly she makes her way back to the sea, leaving behind her in the sand a heavy trail that may last for weeks before the tides wash it away.

The eggs, deep in the sand, are incubated by the warm sun. In about a month or slightly longer, the eggs hatch, and the tiny turtles, about an inch in diameter, struggle out of the sand pit and scramble toward the sea. Those that make the trip at night are safest, for the little turtles are tender, bite-sized morsels for birds and other creatures that comb the beach for their food. Even in the sea, though, they are far from being safe, as they bob about on the surface like corks for many hours. They are unable to submerge until all that remains of the yolk inside their body is digested. Only then do they become full-fledged creatures of the sea.

Two hundred million years ago, long before the days of the dinosaurs, sea turtles made this seasonal trip to land. The hazards to the young then were no fewer than today, and it is surprising that turtles ever survived. But they did—while ichthyosaurs, mosasaurs, and other more spectacular and seemingly better equipped animals became extinct. On land, too, the dinosaurs came and went, as did the mammoths, the ground sloths, and many other animals. Through drastic changes in the earth and its inhabitants, the turtles remained virtually unchanged in basic plan from their most ancient ancestors. Toothless and cumbersome in appearance, turtles would win easily in any "least likely to succeed" contest. But they stand out as one of the most successful animals in the struggle for survival.

Some 230 species of turtles make up this most unusual group of reptiles. Typically their body is almost completely enclosed in a bony shell that protects them like the steel jacket around a tank. Some of the land turtles, in fact, can draw their legs and head inside and shut their shell so tightly, by means of the hinged belly plate, that no amount of thumping, pulling, prying or gnawing can open it. But the largest of all turtles, the marine leatherback, does not have a shell. Its armor consists of seven thick, fatty ridges that run lengthwise down its back. These ridges and the spaces between are covered with a tough, leathery skin. Even without a heavy shell, leatherbacks exceed half a ton in weight, more than twice as much as the largest of today's green and loggerhead turtles. Fresh-water soft-shell turtles also have only a weak shell covered with a flexible leathery skin.

Some tribes of American Indians believed that the weight of the world was supported on a turtle's sturdy back. They used turtle shells to make rattles for ceremonial dances. Until the era of modern plastics, the hawksbill, a medium-sized

Newly hatched leatherbacks run a gauntlet to get from their beach nest to the sea. Waiting here to dine on them are a laughing gull and, in the water, a barracuda.

sea turtle of the Caribbean, supplied a sizable industry with tortoise shell for making combs and pliable jewelry or ornaments. Tortoise shell came from the cut and polished outer layers of the hawksbill's shell. Sometimes the Caribbeans removed the plates by heating the shell of a living turtle and prying the plates loose. They believed the turtle would heal and produce more valuable shell if it were returned to the sea. It is doubtful if many turtles survived the cruel ordeal.

Turtles of many kinds have appealed to man's appetite through the ages. On his second voyage to the New World, Columbus logged his experiences in fishing for sea turtles in the unusual manner practiced by the natives. When a turtle was sighted basking on the surface, a suckerfish, or remora, with a strong line tied to its tail, was let over the side of the boat. Once free the remora headed straight-away for the nearest firm object to which it could attach, and the basking turtle became its target. As soon as the remora had latched onto the turtle, the catch was played up to the boat or into the shallows.

Most sea turtles caught commercially nowadays are trapped in nets. The nets are spread over the potholes where the turtles take refuge to rest, and when the turtles come out to the surface for air, they are caught in the mesh. Big turtles are cut into steaks, and their fat and shells are brewed to make delectable soups and chowders. The harvest has gone on so continuously over the years that there is danger of exterminating the turtles, and protective associations have been formed.

Using its wiggling tongue as a lure, an alligator snapper is about to catch a pumpkinseed sunfish.

Its head and legs hidden in its tightly closed shell, a box turtle is protected from a red fox.

The most famous of all turtles ever used for food were the giant tortoises of the Galapagos Islands off the western coast of South America. Discovered there by early explorers, the huge tortoises lolled in countless numbers on the rock islands. Soon it was learned that they were excellent eating. Equally important, they could be hauled alive in a ship's hold for many months without requiring food or water. Even more incredible, these great bulky beasts stored large quantities of water in pockets beneath the skin of their neck and legs. The water tided them over in the dry months on the islands. Often this same water was a lifesaving source for sailors at sea. An estimated 10 million tortoises were hauled off the islands by whalers and explorers before laws were passed preventing the removal of those few that remained.

Fresh-water turtles of many kinds are relished by man, too. Some restaurants specialize in serving snapping turtles. In other areas the diamondback terrapins are featured. These dinner-plate sized turtles live in brackish waters, and a few years ago, when the turtles were at a peak in popularity, they were nearly exterminated. At one time they sold for as much as 10 dollars apiece.

One of the persistent myths is that turtles live for many centuries. In checking growth rates, biologists learned that a Galapagos tortoise may reach a weight of 400 pounds, about its maximum size, in only 15 years. Sea turtles reach their full size in about 10 years, often tripling their weight in their first two months and reaching a weight of about 100 pounds in five years. Even the largest turtles are probably no more than 30 or 40 years old. But there are several reasonably reliable records of turtles about 150 years old—or about the same age as the oldest record set by man.

Most turtles are much alike in general appearance. As a rule, those with terrible tempers are flesh eaters, while the vegetarians are gentle and make safe pets. Among the most unusual of the turtle clan is the matamata, which lives in the rivers of northern South America. It has small, piggish eyes, and its neck and head are as long as its shell—so long, in fact, that it cannot get them inside the shell but curls them alongside the edge. Flaps and fringes of skin along its head and neck can be moved like lures to attract fish, and when a fish comes close, the turtle gapes its huge mouth and at the same time expands its neck. Water rushes into the opening, sweeping the fish in with it.

Snapping turtles are the largest of the fresh-water turtles in the United States. They can strike with their long neck with the speed of a snake, and their powerful, sharp-edged jaws can snap shut viselike to hold their prey. Alligator snappers, the giants of the group, may weigh a hundred pounds, more than twice the size of the common snapper. Compared to the smaller snappers, however, they are sluggish, though their jaws are powerful enough to sheer a shovel handle in two. To catch fish, they open their mouth and wiggle a pink wormlike appendage that stands up from the front of their tongue, enticing the fish to what it apparently thinks is a worm.

Our language for referring to turtles is oddly garbled. Though there is some confusion about when it is proper to do so, we generally call those turtles that live on land *tortoises.* Edible kinds from fresh or brackish water are called *terrapins,* and *turtle* is the name given all the others that live in the sea or in fresh water. But to commercial turtle fishermen, a sea turtle doesn't rate as a turtle until it tips the scales at more than 100 pounds. Until then, it is called a "chicken."

Two male spotted turtles in a shell-rattling fight.

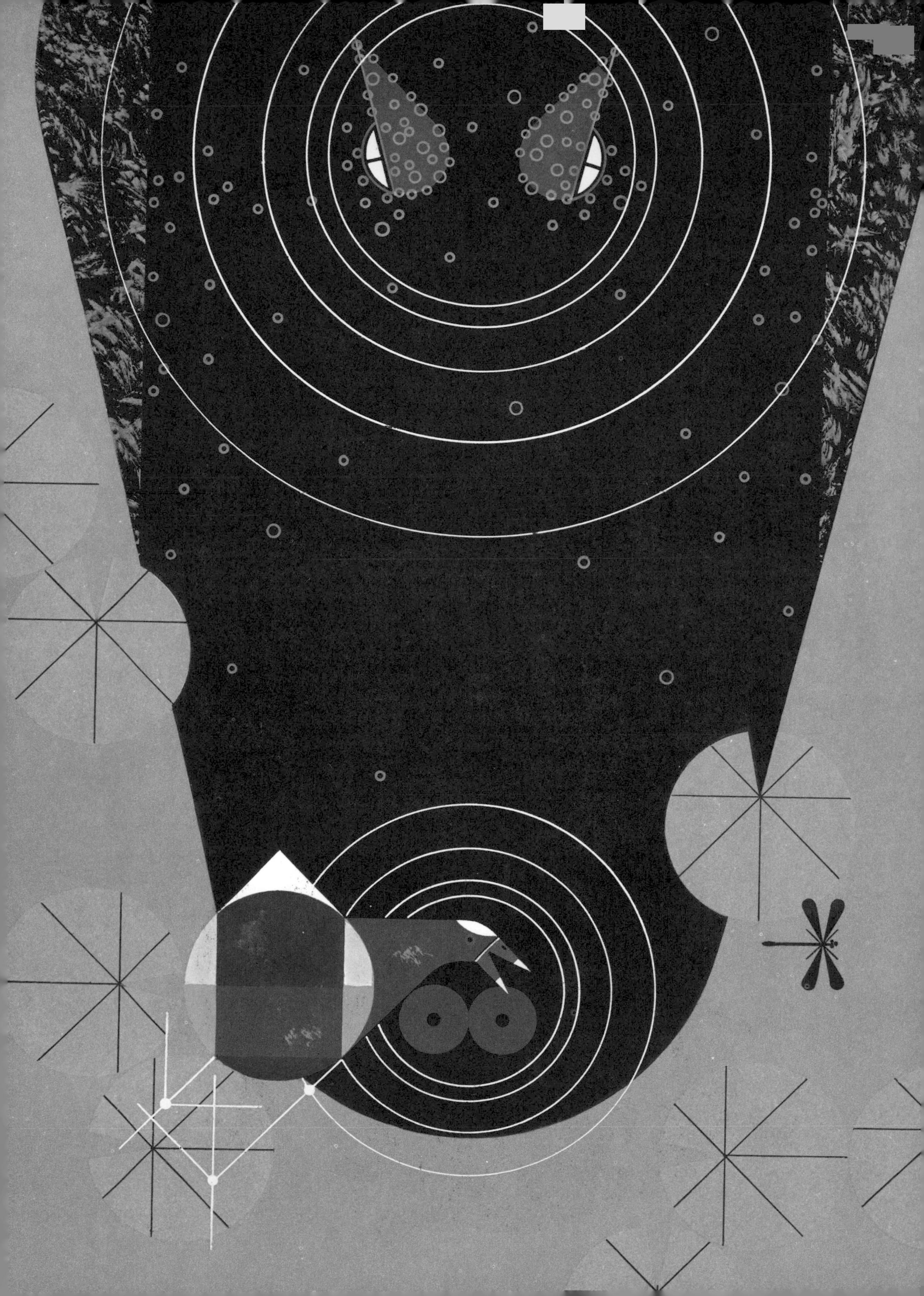

Alligators and Crocodiles

In early spring the booming bellows of bull alligators roll over the swamps of southeastern United States. On otherwise still nights the roars may be heard a mile away. Nearer, the great beasts can be heard hissing and threshing the water with their tail as they pump their body up and down on their short legs and declare their rule over a territory.

If another male ventures on the scene, a bloody battle follows. One of the fighters crawls away wounded, often to his death, while the victor again roars his rule over the swamp. But usually it is a female attracted by the bull's bellows, and when she comes close, she is lured also by a heavy musky odor sprayed from glands beneath the bull's chin.

Later in the spring the female pushes together a mound of vegetation and in its center lays two dozen or more rubbery-shelled eggs. On top of the eggs she piles more vegetation until the mound is as much as three feet high and twice as broad across its base. Then she stands guard nearby, chasing away intruders. The pile of vegetation becomes a natural incubator, heated by decay and by the summer sun. In about two months, the eggs are ready to hatch. One day there is a squeaking from inside the nest as the baby alligators, about eight inches long, rip open their shells. The mother alligator tears away the packed-down vegetation to let them free.

Explorers in America told tales of alligators being so abundant in Florida that they could walk across the rivers on their backs. There are believable records of early-day alligators more than 20 feet long, though today few are longer than 10 feet. Over the years, hunters killed alligators by the millions. Some were slaughtered for food, their thick tail cut into steaks. But mostly they were hunted for their hides, used to make long-wearing wallets, purses, belts, shoes, luggage, and other leather goods. Only the hide over the belly is valuable, as the alligator's back is covered with thick horny plates.

Laws now protect alligators throughout much of their range in the United States, though in some areas those over six feet long can be killed. Most alligators, it is true, are wary and harmless, but those that live near dwellings sometimes become dangerously bold. They have been known to stalk and kill dogs, and worse, especially bad-tempered individuals have also attacked and killed people, particularly children. To their credit, alligators are generally beneficial. They help in mosquito control by keeping open the water channels traveled by gambusias, the tiny fish that feed on mosquito larvae. And alligator holes, dug several feet deep in the grasslands, are often the only source of water for livestock and wildlife during the months of little or no rain in fall and winter.

Alligators cannot be sold for pets in Florida. The animals sold as baby alligators are the very similar and closely related caimans, imported from South America or from the islands of the Caribbean. Caimans have been spared from hide hunters because their belly is covered with ridged plates similar in size to those on their back.

Alligators live in fresh water and range northward into temperate regions. The only other alligators in the world are the now nearly extinct alligators found in China.

Crocodiles, which live in salt water, were once common in the United States, too, but now are very rare. A crocodile's snout is narrow; an alligator's, broad and shovel-shaped. Further, the fourth tooth in a crocodile's lower jaw sticks outside the upper jaw when the mouth is closed. More than a dozen kinds of crocodiles live in tropical salt waters throughout the world. They are generally more pugnacious than alligators, and many have reputations as man-eaters.

Most unusual of the crocodile group of reptiles, which are direct descendants of the ancient dinosaurs, are the slim-snouted gavials of Southeast Asia. They eat mainly fish but also carrion.

An alligator floating on the surface waits and watches, unnoticed by a purple gallinule chasing a damselfly. Instead of eating, the gallinule will be eaten.

Birds

The marvel of birds, distinguishing them from nearly all other animals, is their ability to fly. Bullet-like, a duck hawk drops from the sky on its prey. Said to reach a speed of 175 miles an hour in these dives, it is the fastest of all birds. Other birds have been clocked at 100 miles an hour in level flight. Swallows sweep across the sky in silent, magnificent grace, while grouse explode noisily from the ground and rocket through the air for short distances. As soon as the sun warms the morning air, vultures leave their roost and may soar all day with only an occasional flap of their broad wings. Albatrosses, with long, narrow wings, glide and soar with similar ease over the seas.

A tiny hummingbird, champion of agility in the bird world, can stop in midair to hover at a flower and sip its nectar. It can depart at almost full speed instantaneously and in any direction—up, down, or sideways. Its wings become a buzzing blur, vibrating 50 times or more per second, compared to one beat per second in the deliberate, flapping flight of a pelican. With a refueling stop not even possible, the little ruby-throated hummingbird takes off from the mainland of the United States every autumn and wings its way 500 miles across the Gulf of Mexico to its wintering grounds in tropical America.

Other animals—a few of the prehistoric reptiles, many kinds of insects, and bats among mammals, have mastered flight, but birds are the only group of animals in which flight is the rule rather than the exception. And though with propellers, jets, and rockets, man has flown fast-

A duck hawk plunges into a flock of starlings and grabs a meal in his sharp talons.

er, farther, and higher than birds, he still envies these feathered creatures for their ability to fly under their own power, free and self-controlled. In this respect, man can never match the birds.

Because their flight makes them easy to see and because they are active and have such interesting habits and songs, birds are probably the best known and most popular of all animals. Some species of birds have wide distribution and may be found throughout the world. Others are rare and limited to small areas. The Everglades kite, for example, occurs only in extreme southern Florida, where it nests mainly along the shores of Lake Okeechobee. The kite's only food is a large snail that lives in these wetlands. Many of the approximately 8,500 species of birds have been studied intensively by both scientists and hobbyists, yet much remains to be learned about the habits of most of these fascinating animals.

Fossil records indicate that birds first appeared on earth about 150 million years ago. *Archaeopteryx,* the first of the fossil birds to be found, was quite reptile-like, showing clearly its ancestry. It had a long tail, which present-day birds lack, and it also had teeth in its jaws. Its bones were solid, its breastbone was not enlarged for holding big flight muscles, and three bony, clawed fingers protruded from each wing. *Archaeopteryx* could apparently climb with agility and could probably also soar well. But it is doubtful that it was at all a good flier. This was distinctly just a beginning for birds, but this ancient animal did have feathers, the feature that distinguishes birds from all other animals.

Soft down feathers close to a bird's body serve as insulators, keeping the bird wrapped in a warm layer of air. Over the down feathers are overlapping stiff-veined contour feathers that follow the shape of the bird's body. Still larger flight feathers in the wings and tail form the planing surfaces on which the bird rides through the air. Many birds also have colorful ornamental feathers that form pendants, collars, or crowns on their head, neck, and tail. These may be spread or ruffled to show their colors when the birds court. Some of the most highly decorated are the birds of paradise that live in New Guinea and on nearby islands. The natives of the area used the colorful skins with the plumes attached as items of trade. Europeans liked these fancy feathers, too, and the demand became so great that the birds were almost exterminated. Egrets, ostriches, and other birds with outstandingly beautiful feathers have suffered similar slaughter by plume hunters.

A bird sheds its feathers, or molts, one or more times every year. In most birds, only a few feathers are lost at a time, however, and in matching pairs from each side. In this way the bird's balance and ability to fly are not disturbed. A bird usually becomes less active during the month or so when it is molting most heavily, and contrary to what one would expect, the new plumage of many birds is usually dull at first. It becomes bright and colorful only after the tips of the new feathers have worn away.

Tiny hooks along the front edge of each hair-like filament in a feather hook it to the filament directly in front of it. For this reason each feather forms a strong, solid surface even though it contains countless air spaces. A bird can ruffle its feathers, separating the filaments, and then zipper them together again with its bill. At the same time, many birds can waterproof their plumage by spreading oil over their feathers. The oil is picked up on their bill from a gland near the base of the tail.

While feathers make flight possible and all birds have feathers, not all birds can fly. The 1000-pound elephant bird, largest bird that ever lived, could not fly. It got its name from legends that it could carry off elephants and is believed to have given rise to the Arabian myths about a giant bird called the roc. The elephant bird lived on the island of Madagascar off the east coast of Africa. The giant moa of New Zealand weighed only about 500 pounds but stood 12 feet tall, while the slightly heavier elephant bird was only about 10 feet tall. Both of these giant, flightless birds have been extinct for more than 500 years.

One of the largest and one of the smallest of flying birds: the California condor, with a wingspread of more than nine feet; and the tiny bee hummingbird, only slightly over two inches long.

With its powerful kicks and sharp nails, an ostrich can slash a lion to ribbons.

Ostriches, the largest birds alive today, are also flightless. They stand about eight feet tall and may weigh 300 pounds. Ostriches live in the desert region of central Africa. An ostrich is famous for the fluffy, decorative plumes on its tail and wings. Its egg weighs about three pounds, the largest of all bird eggs. Compared to the size of the ostrich, however, the egg is one of the smallest. The four-pound, chicken-like kiwi of New Zealand, by comparison, lays a one pound egg; this is the largest of all bird eggs in proportion to the size of the bird that lays it.

An ostrich can run about 40 miles an hour, which is fast enough to escape nearly all pursuers. If cornered, the bird does not bury its head in the sand to hide as commonly pictured. Instead, the big bird fights. It can kick powerfully with its two clawed toes, slashing even a lion. Even more formidable is the cassowary of New Zealand and Australia. The cassowary is a shy, retiring bird of the forests, but because it is good to eat, it is sometimes kept around dwellings. When disturbed, a cassowary attacks by leaping and kicking and also uses its bill as a weapon. It has been known to kill people.

Best known of the flightless birds are the penguins of the Southern Hemisphere. They nest along the southern coasts of Australia, New Zealand, South America, Africa, and nearby islands as well as on the icy wasteland of Antarctica. A penguin's wings are flippers with which the birds literally "fly" through the water. The penguin's short, overlapping feathers hug its body so closely they offer no resistance as the bird swims, using its webbed feet for steering. On land a penguin walks with a sedate but comical waddle, or sometimes it scoots along over the snow and ice on its belly.

The emperor penguin, largest of all the penguins, lays its single egg at the beginning of the Antarctic winter rather than in spring or summer. The egg is incubated by the male, who cradles it between his feet to keep it from freezing in the subzero temperature. For the more than two months the male holds the egg in this unusual manner, his mate does not help. She returns from

A swift, skilled swimmer, a jackass penguin closes in on a fish.

the sea, fat from feeding, to take charge of the chick as soon as it hatches. The male, weak and thin from his long siege of incubating the egg, then goes off to fill his stomach on fish, shrimp, or other sea food.

Obviously, it is not feathers alone that make flight possible for birds. Birds that fly have a compact, teardrop-shaped body that offers little head-on resistance to the air in flight. Many of the bones in a bird's body are hollow and filled with air. They are connected to a network of air spaces throughout the bird's body, all of which add to its buoyancy. The bird's ribs are interlocked by means of bony side projections, and other bones are fused to form single, strong units. The bird's breastbone is extended into a broad, flat keel to which the powerful muscles that move the wings are attached. In flightless birds, this keel is small.

In flight, a bird flaps both wings in unison. A possible exception is the chimney swift, for though it does not flap its wings alternately, they beat out of phase so that the bird seems to fly unevenly. In chimney swifts, however, the short, bristly tail is used as a prop to hold them against the sides of a chimney and is of little use for steering, an important fuction of the tail in other birds. So a chimney swift's wings must do most of the steering as well as supplying power. Frigate-birds and some of the kites that have slim, scissor-like tails use their tails to make their agile maneuvers while on the wing.

Birds are warm-blooded animals, unlike the cold-blooded reptiles from which they developed. Flight burns food rapidly, and so to maintain their high body temperature—which in many species exceeds 100 degrees—a bird must eat large amounts of food. Much of a bird's time is spent in searching for food, and young birds are commonly fed more than their weight in food daily. Often a bird's way of obtaining food is revealed by the shape of its bill and by its feet.

A duck's flat, shovel-shaped bill is used to scoop in the mud at the bottom of lakes, ponds, and streams. Water and silt are squirted out through a sieve formed by the toothed edges of the bill when it is closed, and the solid plant or animal food is held inside. A flamingo holds its head upside down and pumps water through its bill as it feeds. Tiny animals caught inside are swallowed. As it feeds, a flamingo prances and shuffles its feet to stir up the mud. Herons, anhingas, kingfishers, and other fish eaters have long, sharp bills for catching fish. The slimmer bills of some of the shorebirds are probes and tweezers for poking into mud or prying into shells.

Hawks, eagles, owls, and other birds of prey use their sharp, hooked bill to grab and to tear flesh. Woodpeckers have a sharp, awl-shaped bill for chiseling into wood. Then they hook grubs or other morsels on the barbs of their long tongue. Cardinals and the many kinds of sparrows crush the hard outer covering of seeds in their stout, wedge-shaped bill. Many birds, and particularly the seed eaters, store food temporarily in their crop, a saclike enlargement of their esophagus. When the stomach digests its contents, more food is spilled into it from the crop. Parrots and their allies have big bills for crushing food

Birds' bills have many shapes and uses.

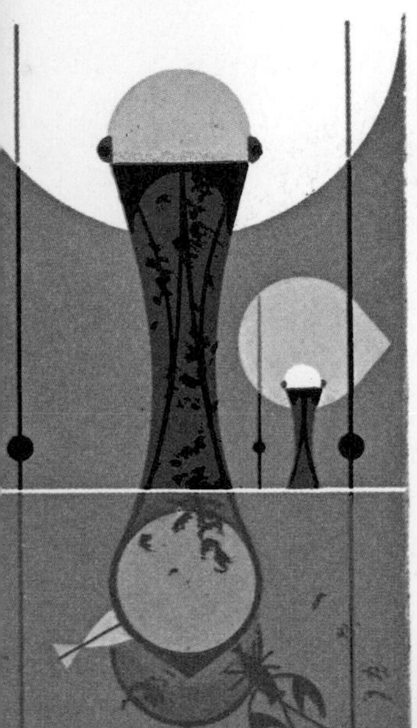

Eurasian spoonbill

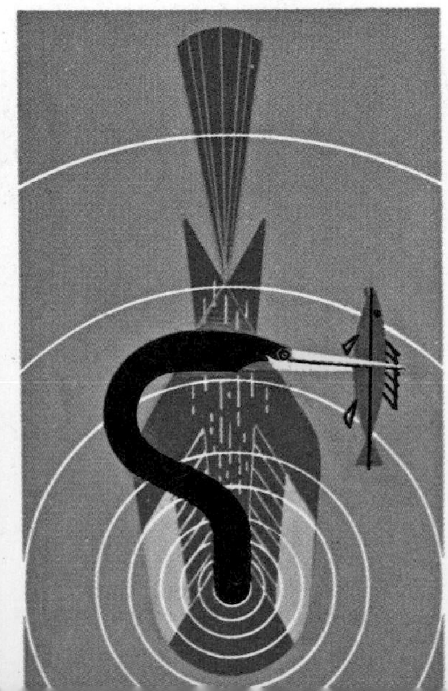

Anhinga

Woodcock

Red-headed woodpecker

Gold-and-blue macaw

Keel-billed toucan

White-winged dove

and skinning tropical fruits. The pouch under a pelican's bill serves as a bag in which fish are trapped and held until they can be juggled into position to be swallowed. A hummingbird's long, slender bill is a probe for dipping deep into flowers for nectar and insects, and the wide bill of nighthawks is an open trap for catching insects while the bird is in flight.

Birds hunt and find their food mainly by sight. Their sense of smell is poorly developed. Vultures are an exception, for it is thought their sense of smell is keen enough to enable them to locate carrion.

The earliest birds, which were much more reptile-like than any of the modern types, had teeth set in bony sockets around the edge of their bill. No bird today has teeth. The lack of teeth, in fact, is another means by which the weight of birds is reduced as an aid to flying. Without teeth, modern birds are not able to chew their food. Instead they grind it in their gizzard, the powerfully muscular hind portion of their stomach. Some birds, and especially those that eat such hard food as seeds, swallow gravel that serves as grinding stones in their gizzard. And the gizzard itself is thick and powerfully muscular, so strong in some birds that they can crack nuts by squeezing together its walls. Hairlike growths in an anhinga's gizzard strain out fish bones.

Like many other animals that hatch from eggs, birds do have an egg tooth. This hard, wedge-shaped bump on the top of the bill is used by the hatchling to chip its way out of its shell. The tooth is shed a few days after the bird leaves the egg.

Brown pelican

Whip-poor-will

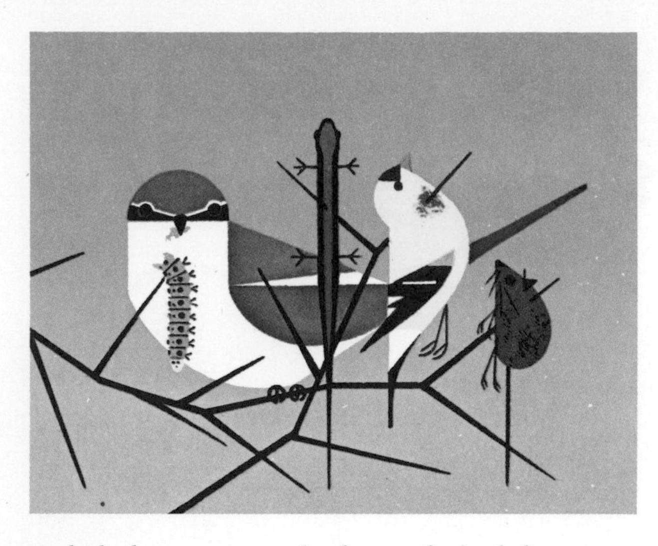

A shrike hangs prey on the thorns of a bush for storage or to help hold it as it is torn apart.

A bird's feet also tell much about its way of life and its method of gathering food. Swimmers, like ducks, geese, and pelicans, have webbed feet. Coots, also swimmers, have rounded lobes of skin along their toes. Hawks, eagles, owls, and other birds of prey have sharp talons with which they grab their prey and hold it as they tear it to pieces. Woodpeckers, nuthatches, and other climbers have powerful toes and sharp nails for clinging to the bark of trees. Chicken-like birds, such as quail and grouse, have stout legs and feet for scratching and digging, while waders have slim, stiltlike legs. Members of the parrot family use their feet like hands to hold and manipulate their food, and also for climbing. Most of the birds that catch their food on the wing have weak legs and feet.

When a perching bird settles down on its roost at night, its toes are locked in their grip on the perch by a special tendon. As long as the bird's weight is pressing down, the tendon remains locked. Most birds use their feet and legs to spring into the air and also to cushion their landing.

Poorwills of western North America hibernate in winter. Many birds that live in cool climates migrate to warmer climates in winter. Some species, such as vultures, do not travel far. They drift southward a few hundred miles or more, often keeping just ahead of the most severe cold weather, then return as the weather warms again. Birds that live high in the mountains in summer commonly move to the low country in winter. And some birds do not migrate at all. When

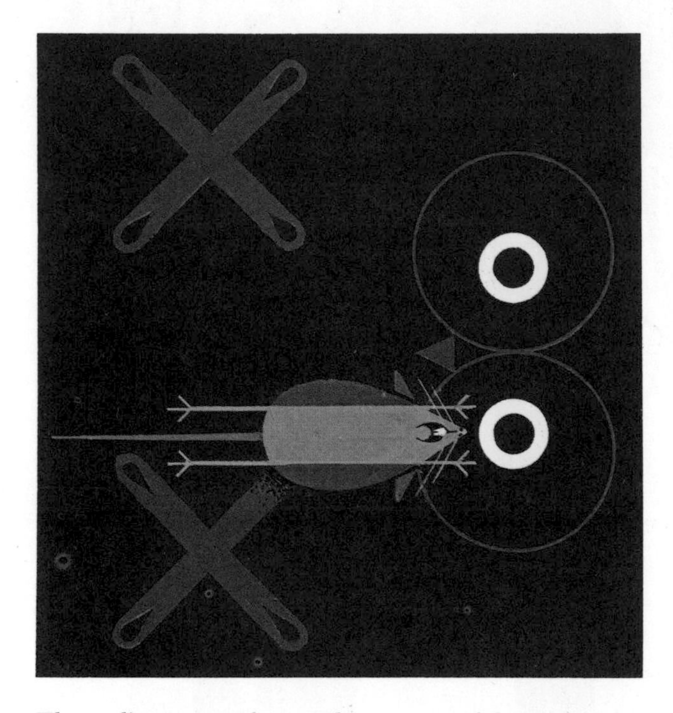

The owl's strong, sharp talons are useful in capturing moving prey, like mice.

A towhee searches the forest floor for insects, scratching vigorously in fallen leaves to stir them up.

Ducks have webbed feet, designed as paddles for swimming.

All these non-migratory birds spend their winters where it snows. They like the birdseed provided by man.
(1) Black-capped chickadee (2) Bluejay (3) Cardinal (4) Tufted titmouse (5) Song sparrow

snow covers the ground and hides their food, these winter residents may starve if food is not put out for them.

Bird banders place a numbered metal or plastic band around a bird's leg and then release the bird. Much has been learned about the distance, speed, and routes followed in migration flights by the return of these bands as the birds are caught or killed later. From returns of bands, for example, the almost unbelievable migration path of the arctic tern has been charted. Many of these sleek sea birds spend their summers near the Arctic Circle, where they nest and rear their young on the tundra. Then they fly southward to winter in the Antarctic. The total mileage traveled each year is about 22,000. The bristle-thighed curlew takes an even longer overseas flight. It nests high in the mountains in Alaska and winters on islands in the mid-Pacific. This requires a flight of about 5,000 miles each way over the sea.

Most familiar of the migrants are the ducks and geese. Their southward flight in autumn heralds the coming of winter. At the same time most of the summer songbirds disappear from their summer nesting ranges and head southward. No one knows exactly what triggers birds to begin their migration flights. Apparently it is related to a decrease in the hours of daylight in autumn that starts them southward, and in spring, the increasing length of daylight sends them north toward their nesting grounds.

Birds sometimes stop migrating when they find an abundance of food or when there is not enough food to give them energy to continue. Bad weather conditions may get them off their course. No one knows, for that matter, how the

This common tern caught in a bander's net will add to what man knows about bird migration.

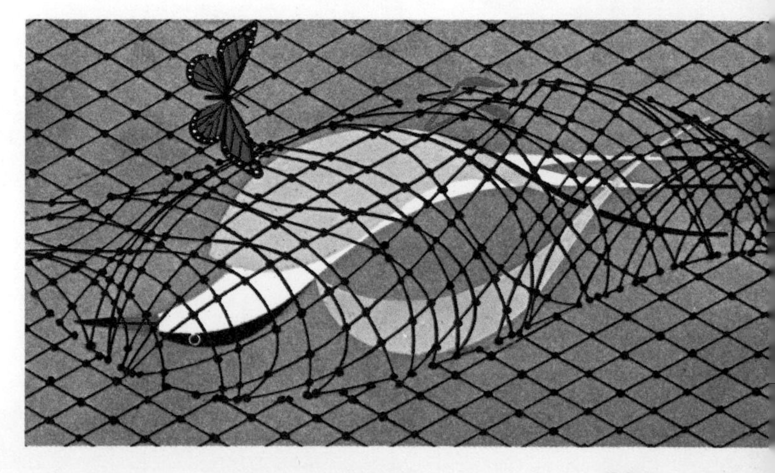

birds know where to go. Young-of-the-year often migrate in groups without leadership of older birds that have made the trip before. Even in flights over water they reach their goal. Much has been learned about migration, but much more remains to be learned before the riddle is solved.

In migration flights, birds generally travel at night, and many do not fly high. TV towers, skyscrapers, and other tall structures take an astonishing toll of migratory birds every season. Birds do fly high, of course, to get over such natural barriers as mountains. Geese have been seen in migratory flights nearly six miles above the earth. Though birds may cover thousands of miles totally in their migration flight, most birds take the trip leisurely, with days of rest following a day of hard travel.

In spring, the birds return to nest. The closer they get to their nesting grounds the faster they travel. Among songbirds, the male usually arrives at the nesting grounds first. The loud, clear calls of birds in spring are those of the males proclaiming their territories and defending them from intruders. Many males build flimsy nests that serve no other purpose than to establish their right to a territory and their intent to nest there as soon as a female is attracted to the site. A male will fight any other male of the same species that invades his territory. His territory is that area which will assure food hunting grounds for him and his mate when they must feed their young.

Some males court the females before mating. They may ruffle their feathers or, if they have them, display their colorful crowns. Others perform "show-off" antics in front of their intended mates. Many strut, bow, and ruffle their feathers. Male woodcocks fly high into the air, spiraling upward until they become mere specks in the sky. Then they turn and dive toward the ground with whistling wings, buzzing out of their plummet just in time to skim the ground. Male hummingbirds of some species zip back and forth in a swinging arc or dives in front of the female of their choice. Their wings vibrate at speeds making them almost invisible, three or four times faster than in normal flight. Prairie chicken males puff up pouches in their neck and make loud booming noises as they let out the air. Many males will gather in one area to perform, spreading their feathers and strutting about as they "boom." Nearby stands an audience of females, their mates to be. Male flamingos do a similar strutting dance before a group of females.

A blue bird of paradise hangs by his feet and spreads his plumage before the female of his choice.

Five male prairie chickens display, boom, and scrap to impress a female who, apparently disinterested, is catching a butterfly.

Other birds court their females by bringing gifts of food or pebbles. Male bowerbirds of Australia and New Guinea make elaborate courtship preparations. Some species construct a walled and roofed-over shelter of vines and sticks. Sometimes the structure is as much as eight feet tall and perhaps six feet in diameter. Inside, the floor and walls are decorated with ferns and moss. Finally the male brings in colorful shells, fruits, and flowers, and if the flowers fade, he replaces them with new ones. A female is lured inside where the male performs his dance. After mating, the female goes off to build an unspectacular shallow nest in which she lays her eggs. She gets no help from her mate.

Each kind of bird builds a nest of the same sort in which it hatched. Females usually take the lead in nest building. The males of some species share the work with the female, and still others do all of the nest building. Some males do not help at all.

Nests of Various Birds

(1) A fairy tern builds no nest and balances egg on a branch.

(2) The long-tailed tailorbird sews two leaves together as a basket to hold nest and eggs.

(3) The ovenbird, one of the many ground-nesters, builds a roofed nest.

(4) Great hornbill uses mud to seal his mate inside a hole in a tree, where she lays her eggs and incubates them. The male feeds her through a small slit.

(5) Barn swallow sticks a cup of mud to the side of barn timbers.

(6) Lesser green broadbill weaves a long sack of grass and roots. It hangs from a branch by a slender strand and has an opening in the side.

(7) Rose-breasted grosbeak's nest is a platform of twigs.

(8) A red-eyed vireo's nest is a neat cup hung in the fork of a branch.

Dove nests are little more than flat, stick platforms. They may be torn apart or the eggs rolled out by a wind. An opposite extreme are the deep pouchlike nests of the weaver birds of Asia and Africa. Some of these bags, woven of vines and other vegetation, contain two rooms—an inner chamber in which a parent bird incubates the eggs and an outer chamber where the other parent stands guard to keep out intruders. As many as 300 pairs of social weavers may occupy the very large, bulky apartment-style nests, which are built by the birds in a community endeavor. The Asiatic tailorbird makes a floor and a roof for its nest by using its bill as a needle and spider silk as thread to sew together two leaves or the edges of one leaf folded over.

Smallest of the bird nests are those of some of the hummingbirds. Woven of bits of moss and lichens, the delicate creations are like little cups. Each nest holds two tiny white eggs. Largest of all nests built by a single pair of birds is credited to eagles. A pair of eagles returns year after year to the same bulky nest of sticks and each year builds the nest higher and broader. A nest in Ohio known to have been occupied for more than 35 seasons measured about eight feet across and was 12 feet deep. Even larger nests, their age not known, have been found in Florida. Among the most interesting of all nests are those of the swifts. These insect-eaters are skilled fliers but have such weak legs that they almost never perch. Instead, they cling to the side of a cliff, to the trunk of a tree, to the inside of a chimney or to some similar vertical surface. Their nests are glued to these surfaces with the bird's saliva. Palm swifts stick their eggs in a flat nest of plant fibers and feathers against a palm frond or the leaf on a similar plant. Others build their nests of mud, moss, and twigs, sticking them to the rocky sides of cliffs, inside hollow trees or in similar places. And a group of swiftlets that live in the Orient make their nests almost wholly of saliva. The nests of these swiftlets are collected, processed, and sold as a food delicacy in China.

Some birds build no nest at all and simply lay their eggs on the ground. Vultures lay their eggs in hollow logs or in rocky crevices. Nighthawks lay their eggs on the ground or on pebbled rooftops. Auks lay their eggs on rock ledges. Some kinds of swallows dig holes in dirt banks and put their eggs in a chamber at the end. Kingfishers and burrowing owls are among the other kinds of birds that nest in tunnels. Woodpeckers lay their eggs in cavities chiseled in the trunks of trees. And some birds lay their eggs in the nests of other birds, letting the host incubate the eggs and rear the young. Among these parasites are the European cuckoo and the cowbirds of North America.

A female cowbird approaches another bird's nest stealthily and waits until the intended host has departed to feed. The cowbird swiftly deposits her egg in the nest and then departs. The cowbird egg is usually larger than the other eggs in the nest, and the time needed to incubate it is only about 10 days. For this reason the young cowbird often hatches several days before

Burrowing owls nest in tunnels in the ground.

These bird eggs are about actual size and from the largest to the smallest: ostrich, emu, king penguin, murre, barn owl, tinamou, robin, magnolia warbler, and broad-billed hummingbird.

the eggs of the host bird. The young cowbird is large and demands much food. Even if the other eggs in the nest do hatch, the young birds are commonly shoved out by the squirming, squawking young cowbird.

Eggs hatch only after a period of incubation. Mostly this is a matter of keeping them warm while the embryo develops, but if the eggs would otherwise be exposed to a blazing sun, as would those laid in sand or on open rocks, they may be kept covered to keep them cool. Generally a bird that is incubating eggs develops bare patches where the eggs come in direct contact with the skin. Most commonly the female does the incubating, but in some species the male also helps. In a few, the male does the incubating by himself.

Eggs of most songbirds hatch in about two weeks. Some of the albatrosses incubate their eggs for nearly three months, and even tiny hummingbird eggs generally do not hatch for about three weeks. Birds do not sit on the eggs constantly during this time, of course. Some are away from the eggs as much as a fourth of the time finding food for themselves. Males of some species bring tidbits to their mates as they sit on the eggs. The young of many ground-dwelling birds are well-developed when they come from the egg. They are covered with down feathers and can run about immediately in search of food or to escape enemies. These young birds are called precocial. Newly hatched ducklings, for example, can swim. Young ducklings, and also swans, geese, and grebes, ride their mother's back like a raft to rest or to bask in the sun. As they break out of the shell, quail shake themselves dry and soon begin running after their mother.

Many young birds are naked, blind, and helpless at hatching. These are called altricial young. They are cared for in the nest for several days or weeks, usually for about as long as it took to incubate the eggs. These young birds are obviously not fully developed. The head is large for the size of the body, and the mouth is enormous. Generally the bill is a bright yellow, and

The newly hatched clapper rail, above, is precocial—ready to run the instant it comes from the egg. The hatchling catbird, below, is altricial and will need weeks of feeding and protection from its parents.

the lining of the mouth is colored. Apparently these bright colors aid the parent in finding the young bird's mouth to feed it. At first the young are fed on partly digested food from their parent's crop. Pigeons produce in their crop a cheeselike substance, called "pigeon's milk," that nourishes the newly hatched birds. As young birds grow larger their demands become greater. One or both parents are kept busy throughout the daylight hours hunting worms, insects, seeds or other food to keep the baby birds satisfied. Not uncommonly a parent visits the nest with food every two or three minutes all during the daylight hours. The parents also keep the nest clean of droppings and try to defend the young from attackers.

The young birds leave the nest as soon as their flight feathers are grown. Many songbirds, such as the grackles, stay together in family groups or flocks. Other birds, such as the hawks for example, drive their young away to lead a solitary life until the next nesting season.

The songs of birds are distinctive and in many species are as useful in identification as their plumage, body shape, or flight pattern. A few kinds, such as the vultures, are voiceless, and many of the sea birds are virtually so. The calls and songs of birds serve definite puposes. They may rally the members of a flock, warn of danger, or advertise claim over a nesting territory. Some kinds of birds sing all year, others only at mating time. Many songbirds select particular perches from which to sing and move from one perch to another following a circuit through their territory. Often this pattern is so definite that almost the exact time of their appearance on a perch can be predicted. Mockingbirds are mimics, copying the songs of other birds, and they may continue to sing all through the night. Parrots and mynahs are famous mimics that can learn to talk. Not all birds are melodious, however. Many scream raucously or produce other weird sounds that are not at all pleasing to our ears.

The sounds a bird makes, whether melodious warbling or loud trumpeting calls, are produced at the end of its windpipe, in a structure called the syrinx. Its tongue has little or nothing to do with its calls and songs.

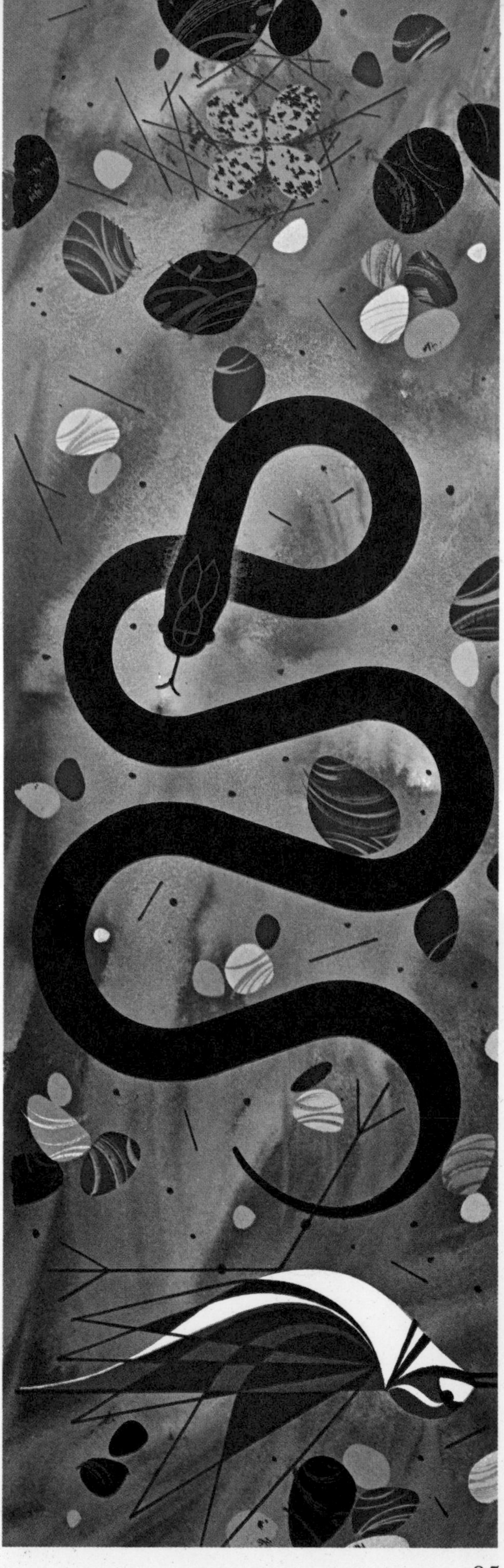

A mother killdeer feigns injury to lure a black ratsnake away from her eggs.

Mammals

From all over the world people travel to Africa to see the big animals for which that continent is so famous. Binoculars flash in the sun and cameras click and whir as safari wagons roll across the savannas. In hushed awe people watch from treetop platforms over trails and at water holes.

Elephants, hippos, giraffes, zebras, lions, vast herds of antelopes—all of these magnificent mammals are there to see, but their numbers are fast dwindling. This is due in part to hunting, but it is due mostly to the shrinking of the wilderness areas by the spreading settlements of man, himself a mammal. Big animals need large areas in which to roam and to find their food, and so slowly these most spectacular of all land animals are being squeezed out of living space. For many of Africa's big animals, the last strongholds are the giant parks so wisely being set aside to satisfy their needs. The largest of the network so far is Kruger National Park in southeastern Africa. It is a strip of land 30 to 40 miles wide and 250 miles long, covering nearly 9,000 square miles.

All of these colorful, most spectacular animals of Africa are mammals, the group that include such familiar animals as dogs, cats, horses, cows, rats, mice, and man. Like birds, mammals are warm-blooded—that is, they have a constant, high body temperature. Most mammals have thick, furry hair, their distinctive feature, but some kinds are nearly hairless. Man has only a spotty covering of hair. The few hairs on an elephant are as heavy as fence wire. Whales and armadillos have only a few bristles. But all mammals have hair at least at some time during their life. Mammals feed their young on milk from mammary glands, from which the name for the group is derived.

The more than 15,000 kinds of mammals range

in size from the tiniest of the shrews and bats less than two inches long to the gigantic blue whales that weigh 100 tons. All are alike in basic features, yet each group and each kind is clearly set apart from all others. There are three main divisions: the monotremes, the marsupials, and the placentals.

Monotremes, the most primitive, are the only mammals that lay eggs, which are surrounded by a shell like those of reptiles. These are the two kinds of spiny anteaters, or echidnas, and the platypus, found only in Australia, New Guinea and on nearby islands. Spiny anteaters are strictly land dwellers. The female lays one egg in a pouch on her belly. After hatching, the young stays inside the pouch until it becomes too prickly for the mother to carry comfortably.

The platypus lives in burrows along the banks of ponds and streams. It has a broad tail and webbed feet for swimming and feeds on grubs and worms rooted from the mud with its flat, ducklike snout. The female makes a nest lined with leaves and grass and incubates her eggs by holding them close to her body. In both the platypus and spiny anteaters, milk seeps from the scattered glands into hairy pockets from which it is lapped up by the nursing young.

Only slightly less primitive are the marsupials, or pouched mammals. All of the several species of opossums in the Americas are marsupials. Newborn opossums are no larger than a bee or a wasp and are still quite immature. Feebly they crawl along a slime track to the mother's pouch where they complete their development. Each baby remains fastened to its mother for about a month before it begins to move about on its own. For another month it continues to nurse and still uses the pouch as a place in which to hide. All American opossums have a scaly, hairless tail which they use as an aid in climbing. When frightened, the common or Virginia opossum of North America "plays dead," lying motionless until danger is past.

Except for a few species of rat opossums found in western South America, all the other marsupials live in Australia or nearby islands. The

A pride of lions keeps a respectful distance while a zorille, an African weasel with a more potent odor than a skunk, examines their freshly killed zebra.

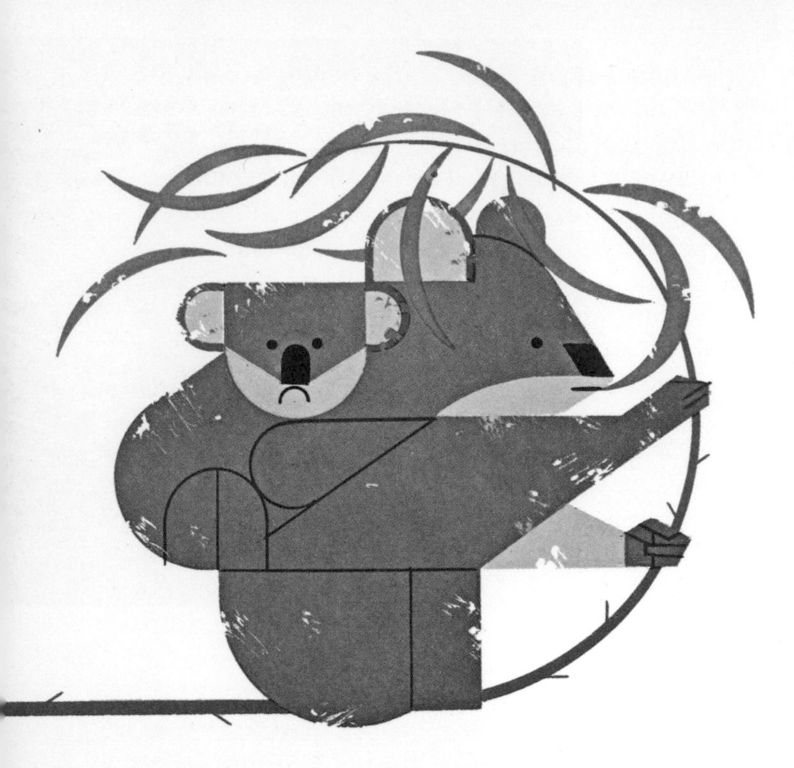

A mother koala and her baby in a eucalyptus tree. The tree's leaves are the koala's only food.

giants are the kangaroos. Some kinds stand seven feet tall and can leap 20 feet in one bound, traveling 25 to 30 miles an hour. The female kangaroo carries her young, called a "joey," for as long as six months before it is large enough to leave her pouch and go its own way. Not all kangaroos and their close relatives are large, however. Musk kangaroos are no bigger than rats. Wallabies are about the size of rabbits.

Many of the great variety of pouched mammals of Australia resemble mammals that live in other parts of the world. There are pouched mammals that look like dogs or wolves. Others are spotted or striped and are similar to skunks. There are many small mouselike marsupials, and a group of burrowers are like moles. The phalangers, very much like North American flying squirrels, are excellent climbers and gliders. Wombats are similar to badgers. Koalas are not much larger than the cuddly teddy bears they look like. They feed exclusively on the leaves of some kinds of eucalyptus trees and for this reason are difficult to rear in captivity.

Millions of years ago pouched mammals were much more widespread in the world. They could not compete successfully with the more highly developed placental mammals, however, and so they survived in numbers only in the isolation of Australia and nearby islands. In placental mammals, which includes most present-day mammals, the unborn young are nourished through a special tissue, the placentum.

Shrews, moles, and hedgehogs are small, secretive insect eaters. Tiny shrews are abundant but seldom seen. Most shrews live in leaf litter or in loose soil. Frequently they prowl mouse runways or mole burrows. Water shrews are good swimmers and can also scamper across the water's surface. Shrews are so active they burn their food at a rapid rate and must eat constantly to keep from starving to death. A shrew's normal fare is insects, but it will attack fearlessly animals that are more than twice its size. The saliva of some shrews is poisonous enough to kill prey.

A mole's front legs are broad, flat paddles enabling the animals literally to swim through the soil. The mole's very small eyes probably serve only to distinguish light from dark. Moles live in deep, underground chambers, but they also dig burrows close to the surface to feed on grubs and worms found mainly around the roots of plants. Unfortunately, they may upset tender young plants in gardens as they bulldoze their way underground in search of food. The unusual

star nosed mole has a cluster of sensitive, fleshy feelers forming a rosette at the tip of its snout.

European hedgehogs, well-known in legends, roll into a ball when frightened, tucking both head and feet inside. Hedgehogs eat insects, worms, and other small animals. Stories persist that hedgehogs collect apples or other fruit on their sharp spines, either catching them as they fall from the tree or impaling them by rolling on them. Most authorities agree that any apple caught on a hedgehog's back is there strictly by accident and that it will not be eaten unless it is obviously full of worms.

(1) A greater glider, one of the flying phalangers, is a marsupial mammal of Australia.

(2) Female platypus, with eggs in underground nest.

(3) The mother kangaroo's pouch opens to the front, which helps keep the baby inside when she is traveling fast.

(4) The mother bandicoot's pouch opens to the rear, important to the babies when she is digging for food. Bandicoots are rabbit-sized marsupials.

A vampire bat laps blood from the paw of a sleeping capuchin.

Bats are the only mammals capable of true flight. Their wings are thin membranes stretched between their long fingers and their body and, in some, also between the tail and the body. Only their clawed thumb is free and movable. Bamboo bats are only about an inch and a half long; giant "flying foxes" have a wingspread of five feet. Some bats are pugnosed; others have a long pointed snout. Some have a long, barbed tongue for dipping deep into flowers for nectar. Some have neat, rounded ears; in others the ears are twice the size of the head. Most bats feed either on insects, nectar, or fruit, but some have special diets. Fish-eating bats of tropical America skim the surface of water and pick up small fish. Vampire bats of the American tropics have razor-sharp teeth with which they can slit the skin and drink the blood of victims without even waking them.

Bats are nocturnal, using their remarkable natural radar system, or echo-location, to navigate in the dark. Bats make easily heard squeaking noises like mice, but in flight, they also give off a pulsing rhythm of high-pitched sounds that are beyond the hearing range of the human ear. When these sound pulses hit objects, they echo back and are picked up by the bat's sensitive ears. In this way the bat can tell what lies ahead. But no one knows how the bats determine which of these echoes come from objects they should avoid and which of the echoes come from insects or from other food.

Most bats sleep during the day and feed at night. The insect eaters catch their food in flight. Bats that live where the winters are cold either hibernate or migrate southward. Large numbers may collect in caves, hollow trees, or the attics of buildings. By far the majority of the nearly 1,000 species of bats live in the tropics.

Most abundant of all mammals are the rodents, or gnawers. A rodent's chisel-like front teeth never stop growing. They are kept sharp and worn

(1) An age old story is written in snow—a dog chases a rabbit. (2) A capybara, largest of all rodents. (3) A mountain lion's paw is like a pincushion after encountering a porcupine. (4) Chisel-toothed beaver downs a tree.

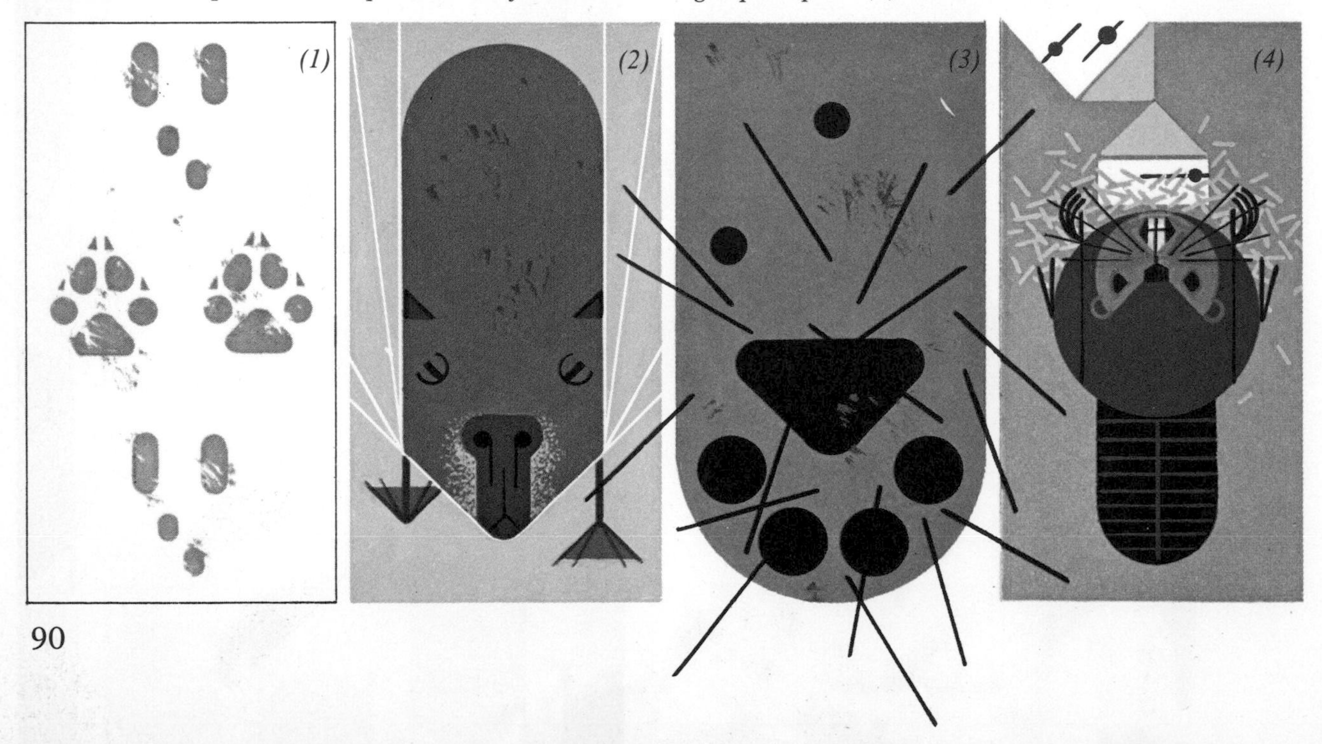

down by gnawing on stems, roots, nuts, or other hard objects.

The house mouse, Norway rat, and black rat, found throughout the world, have traveled with man wherever he has settled. Many mice and rats are really attractive little creatures. All of the nearly 200 species of white-footed, or deer mice, of North America are bright-eyed and immaculately decked in rich reds, browns, or grays, with snowy white underparts. Nearly all mice and rats feed on plants, eating seeds, stems, or roots. A few kinds are flesh eaters. Grasshopper mice stalk their insect prey like cats in turn stalk mice. Even scorpions are accepted on this little mouse's menu. If insect hunting goes poorly, it will stuff its stomach with seeds.

Pack rats, or wood rats, most abundant in western North America, fill their nests with all sorts of items, preferring shiny ones. They are notorious for their visits to cabins, where they raid the cupboards and closets. Usually they leave a nut, a pine cone, or a rock in trade for what they have stolen. Often they surround their bulky nests with clumps of cactus spines, which discourage larger animals from entering.

Meadow mice, or voles, are short-tailed rodents that live in the temperate to cold regions of the Northern Hemisphere. Lemmings of Scandinavian countries are voles familiar for the tales about their suicidal migrations to the sea. In some years, following a definite cycle, the population of lemmings becomes very large. When all of the food in their area is eaten, the lemmings move to a new territory. There, with the number of lemmings suddenly doubled, the food is quickly depleted, too, and so the lemmings move again. Soon the countryside swarms with millions of scurrying, hunger-driven migrants. Rivers, fiords, or the sea itself are plunged into without hesitation. Most of the little furry animals drown.

The muskrat, largest of all voles, digs burrows in the banks of streams, ponds or lakes. In marshes it may build a clumpy nest of leaves and stems above the water level. In the vast swamplands at the mouth of the Mississippi and in a few other areas in the country, the muskrat must compete now for living space with a rapidly spreading newcomer—the nutria, or coypu. Nutria were introduced to the United States from

A migrating lemming falls prey to a snowy owl.

South America as caged animals but escaped. These unusual rodents are twice the size of musk-rats and have orange-red teeth. The female's mammary glands are located high on her sides, allowing the young to nurse as the mother swims.

The size and variety of rodents is seemingly endless. Some of the most attractive of the gnaw-ers are the red mice of southeastern Asia and the golden-yellow hamsters of Europe and Asia. An African rat is more than three feet long. Desert-dwelling jerboas of Africa and jumping mice of North America have large, powerful hind legs and can jump like kangaroos. A tiny mead-ow jumping mouse less than four inches long can jump more than 10 feet. Largest of all the rodents is the South American capybara, which stands nearly four feet tall and weighs more than 75 pounds.

North American beavers feed on the inner bark of shrubs and trees, which they cut down with their powerful teeth. They use the branches and trunks with rocks and mud, combining them in building their dams. As the pool of water builds up, the beavers build the dam higher and longer. Beaver dams more than 10 feet thick and nearly as tall have been found, and one in the West was nearly half a mile long! Such large dams are the work of many beavers. In the pool behind the dam, the beavers build their den, or lodge, which has an underwater entrance. Green branches are stored in the pool for winter food.

All the many kinds of tree squirrels, another huge family of rodents, are skilled climbers. Their bushy tail serves as a balancer and as a rudder for steering. Like other rodents, squirrels store hoards of food. They bury nuts on the for-est floor or tuck them into hollows in trees—and then forget where most of them are. Many kinds of squirrels live in the tropics. Some are no larger than mice, others more than three feet long. The so-called "flying" squirrels have a thin flap of skin between their front and hind legs along the sides of their body. With this mem-brane stretched taut, flying squirrels can glide hundreds of yards. The flying squirrels of North America are small, graceful creatures six to nine inches long. The giant flying squirrels of southern Asia may be three feet long. Chipmunks, go-phers, prairie dogs, and marmots, the most familiar of which is the woodchuck or ground-hog, are ground-dwelling members of the squir-rel family.

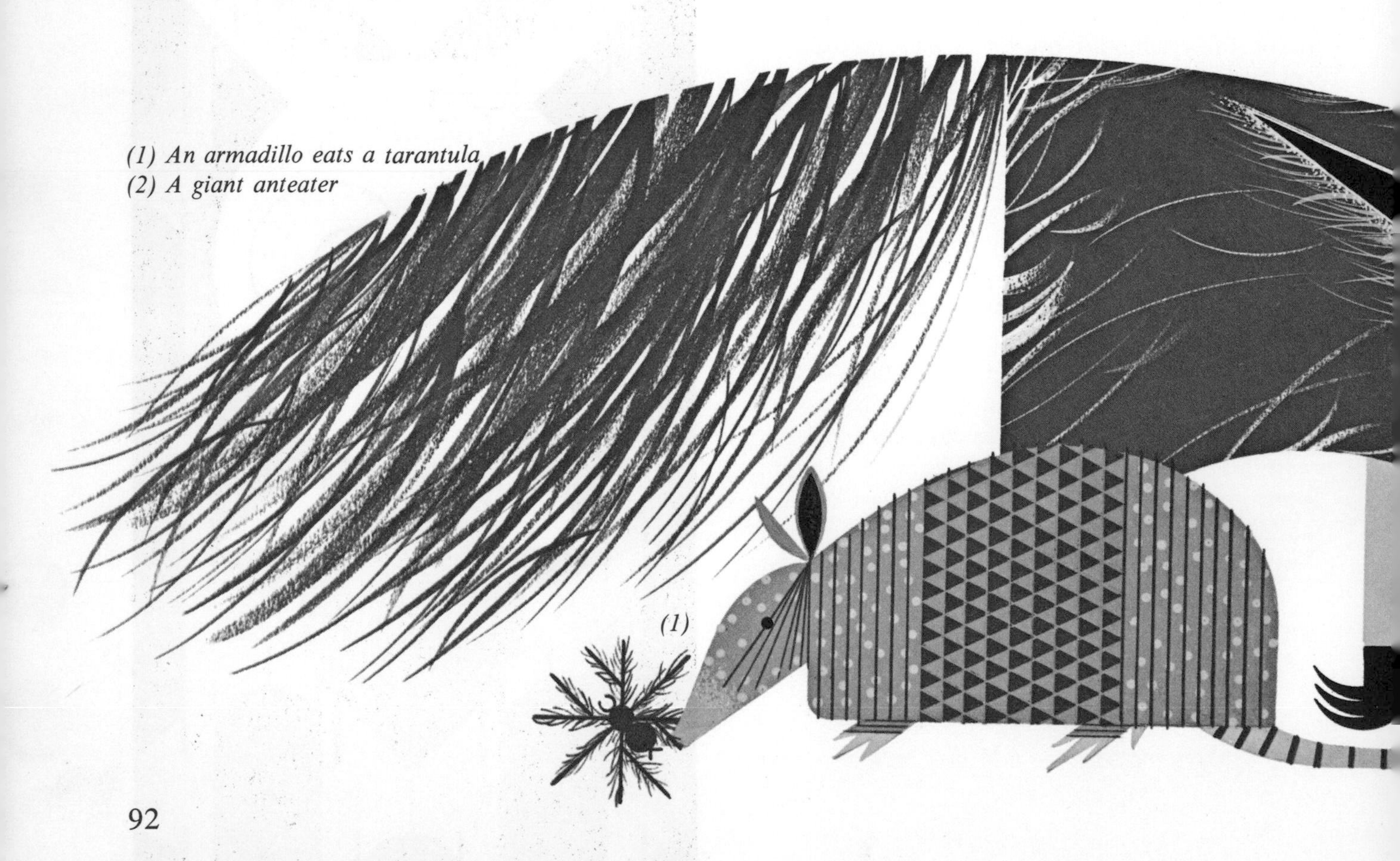

(1) An armadillo eats a tarantula
(2) A giant anteater

Porcupines are rodents that bristle with quills as sharp as thorns. A porcupine does not shoot its quills, but when alarmed, the animal lifts its quills so that they form a spiny barrier between itself and an intruder. It may also lash its tail, and pity the poor animal that gets close enough to be struck.

Rabbits and hares resemble rodents but have two pairs of front teeth in the upper jaw rather than only one. Rabbits are born naked, helpless, and with closed eyes. Hares are born with their eyes open and with fur. They can move about soon after birth. Jack rabbits of North America are really hares. Some kinds can leap 20 feet in a single bound and are said to be able to run more than 45 miles an hour. They depend on

A pangolin escapes a tiger by curling up inside its armor.

Water drains rapidly off a sloth's "upside down" hair.

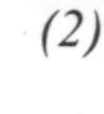

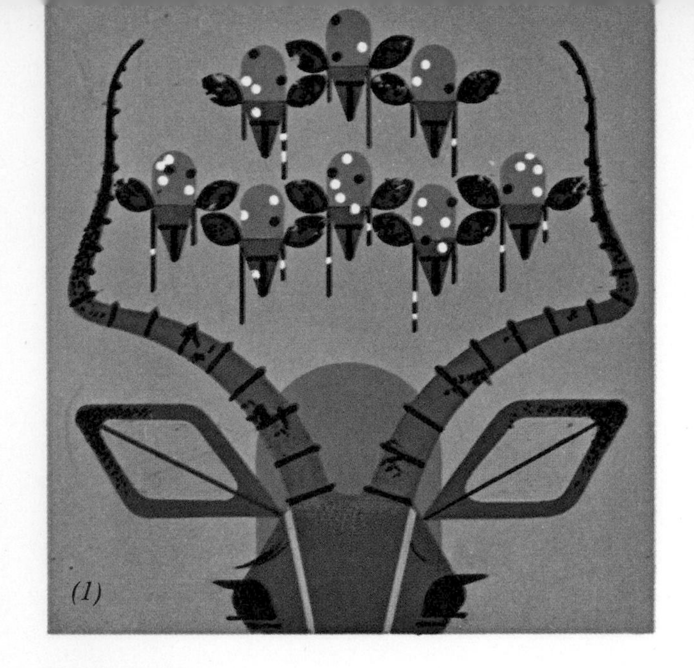

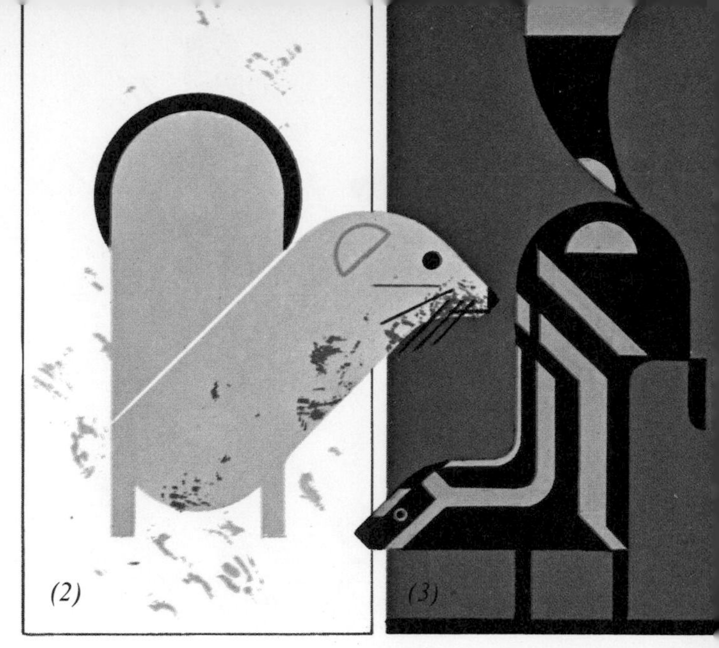

their speed to escape enemies in the prairie country where they live. Cottontails, or rabbits, are much smaller and less fleet. Both rabbits and hares have mild dispositions, though they will defend their young in the nest against animals larger than themselves. Tiny pikas, or conies, are rabbit relatives that live among the rocks high in the mountains throughout the Northern Hemisphere.

Among the most unusual of all mammals are the toothless anteaters, armadillos, and sloths. Anteaters walk with the enormous claws on their front feet turned under. They use their claws to tear apart ant and termite nests, then collect their meal on their long, sticky tongue. The anteaters of Central and South America are hairy animals; pangolins, the anteaters of the Old World, are covered with scaly plates.

Sloths, the most sluggish of all mammals, hook their long, curved claws over a limb and hang upside down. In the same position, they move along the branch at a slow pace. Found only in the American tropics, the sloth turns green in the rainy season due to heavy growths of algae in its hair. A ground-dwelling sloth extinct now for millions of years was bigger than an elephant.

Armadillos are covered with scaly plates like a turtle, but here and there between the plates are bristly hairs. Some armadillos roll into a ball, tucking all of their soft parts out of sight. One kind ducks into a burrow and plugs the entrance with the thick plate over its tail. The nine-banded armadillo, found from Central America to southern United States, gives birth to quadruplets. Young armadillos have a soft skin; they do not get their hard plates for two or three months.

Aardvarks of Africa look something like an armadillo without armor but are not related. Aardvarks eat ants and termites and can dig rapidly. Their Dutch name means "earth pig."

Top position in most food cycles is occupied by a flesh-eating mammal, or carnivore. Nearly all of the many kinds have strong, sharp teeth for holding their prey. Most can move swiftly, have sharp claws, and excellent eyesight.

Bears, found on all continents except Australia, are the largest of the carnivores. Kodiak bears may weigh more than 1,500 pounds, while grizzly and polar bears weigh nearly as much. All bears walk with a shuffling, flat-footed gait. Most bears supplement their diet of fish or meat with berries, nuts, grass, fruit, or even seaweeds. Bears do not hibernate in winter, but they sleep for long periods when the weather is bad. They awaken several times during the winter and may emerge to feed if the weather permits.

Raccoons are easily recognized by their black mask and ringed tail, a feature shared with their American relatives, the coatis and cacomistles, and with the panda of Asia. Raccoons hunt for crayfish, frogs, and other animals along the shores of ponds, lakes, and streams. They are noted for "washing" their food—dunking it in water, perhaps to help soften it.

Reigning member of the dog family in the Northern Hemisphere is the wolf, pushed nearly to extinction by civilization. A full-grown wolf may weigh more than 150 pounds. In winter, when food is harder to find, hungry wolves often band

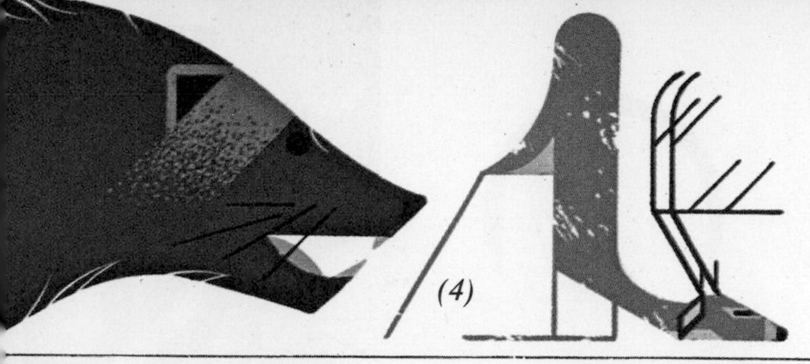

(1) Cape hunting dogs pursue an impala. (2) Short-tailed weasel emerges from a mouse hole where it just dined on the mouse. (3) The spotted skunk does a hand-stand to warn invaders before releasing gas attack. (4) Wolverines will trail prey until the animal drops from exhaustion. (5) Badgers are the kings of the diggers.

together in packs and will hunt down animals as large as caribou.

The wail of the coyote signifies the American West. This small wolf was labeled by sheepmen as an incurable killer, and so large numbers of coyotes have been poisoned and shot. Coyotes eat mainly mice and other small rodents, which do more damage than the few killer coyotes.

Other wild members of the dog family are the Australian dingo, which may have originated from domestic dogs turned loose or escaped from early visitors to that continent; the carrion-eating jackals of Africa and Asia; the Cape hunting dogs of Africa and the dholes of India, both famed for hunting in packs. The raccoon dog of China looks and acts like a raccoon and has the disturbing habit of howling at the moon. The many kinds of foxes all have a reputation for cunning. Red foxes, the elusive quarry of hunters for centuries, are abundant both in Europe and America. They live successfully in the woods and fields of farm country. Gray foxes are more catlike and less daring. The several kinds of big-eared foxes that

A playful otter shoots "white water" rapids.

live in deserts are noted for their speed and ability to dodge quickly to throw off a pursuer. Man's "best friend"—the domestic dog—also belongs to this family of flesh eaters. Hyenas, doglike but members of a separate family, feed mainly on carrion, crushing bones with their strong teeth.

Weasels are sleek and almost snakelike in their movements. An ermine is a weasel that gets a white winter coat. Many weasels are bloodthirsty, killing not only for food but apparently for pleasure. The mink is a large weasel that lives in and near water. Martens, fishers, and wolverines are members of the weasel family. Wolverines, though only four feet long, may attack and kill a caribou. They raid cabins and turn their contents topsy-turvy; they also rob traps of their catches. People of the North Country use the coarse wolverine fur to trim parkas, for it does not collect moisture and freeze.

Badgers, also of the weasel family, live in upland areas. They can dig so rapidly they seem to melt out of sight. Nearly all members of the weasel family have musk glands that give off a strong odor, but only the skunks can fire the spray with accuracy. They do so only when other efforts to discourage an intruder have failed. The strong odor may carry for more than a quarter of a mile, and a direct hit can blind an attacker.

Otters, the most streamlined of the weasel family, spend most of their time in water. River otters, widely distributed in North America, may travel 15 to 20 miles in a night visiting ponds and streams to catch fish. Otters fight courageously if cornered. They rarely get in such a predicament though, as they are swift swimmers and may stay submerged for long periods of time. Otters are playful, often making a mud slide down a bank into the water near their den or in the snow in winter. Whole families participate in the play, each taking a turn going down the slide. Sea otters, larger cousins of the river otters, live in the North Pacific. They rarely come ashore, even resting and sleeping while holding onto mats of kelp.

A black leopard's whiskers (above) gauge the opening through which it can pass in undergrowth.

A walrus (below) uses its tusks to hoist its own massive weight out of the water and onto the ice.

Civets, genets, and mongooses are slender-bodied animals in a family with representatives throughout the Old World. All have strong scent glands. The mongoose is known for its fearless attacks on cobras. It agitates the deadly snake to strike, then dodges. As the cobra falls to the ground, the mongoose grabs the reptile by the head and kills it. The mongoose is also a good rat exterminator.

Cats are lithe, graceful carnivores that typically spring on their prey. They use their sharp, hooked claws to help hold their victim and also to help tear it apart. Most cats can retract their

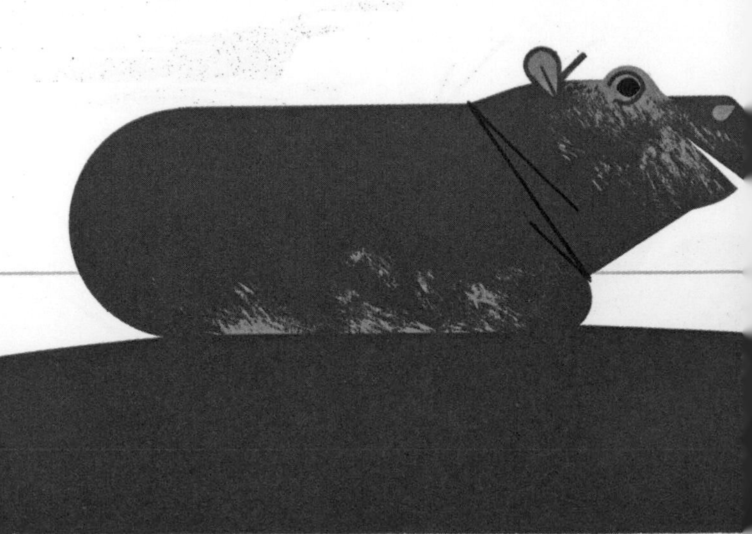

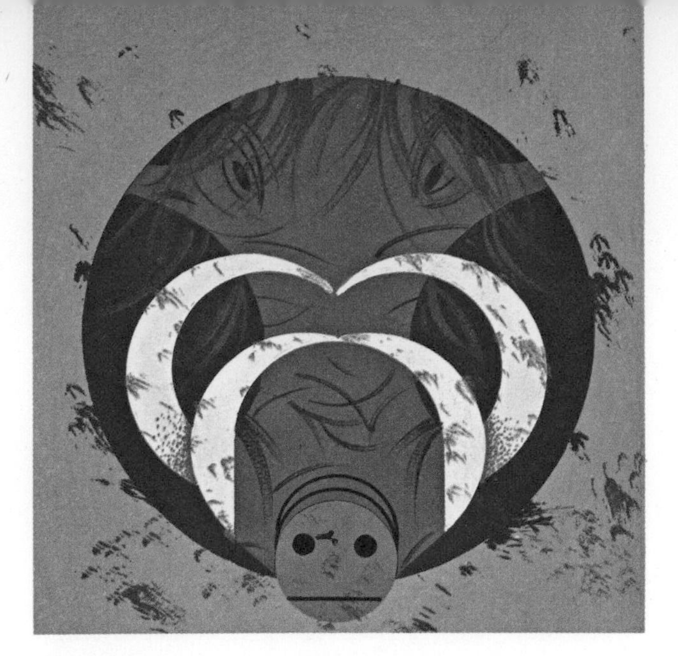

The warthog backs into his underground home.

An African lion rules as king of the beasts more by appearance than by fierceness. Sporting a shaggy mane, the male lion has an unsurpassed air of regal dignity. Lions are unafraid of other animals but rarely kill solely for the sake of killing. They take what they need and return to feast on the remains until all has been eaten. Lions commonly travel in small bands, or prides, consisting of several females and their offspring and a strong, young male. Tigers of Asia are nearly as large as lions. Both of these big cats are occasionally man-killers, but killer cats are generally older animals that are too feeble to catch their natural prey. They turn to man only because he is easier to overcome.

Leopards, smaller than either the lion or the tiger, range from the lowlands to the high mountains in Asia and parts of Africa. There are several color forms of leopards. Still smaller are

claws into sheaths when not in use. The exception is the long-legged cheetah, swiftest of all the cats. A cheetah can run 70 miles an hour for short distances and can be trained to run down antelopes for hunting parties.

Cats have sharp fangs for holding their prey but have poor grinders. Their tongue is rough and filelike. A cat's eyes are large, adapting it for night hunting, and its sense of hearing is acute. Their long, sensitive whiskers serve as feelers. Cats do not hunt by smell as much as do dogs.

The largest cat in North America is the mountain lion (cougar, puma, or panther), restricted now to wilderness tracts. The jaguar, nearly twice as large, is most plentiful along waterways in the American tropics.

Tick birds take their meals of insects off a rhino.

A baby hippo riding on his mother's back is safe from the cruising crocodile.

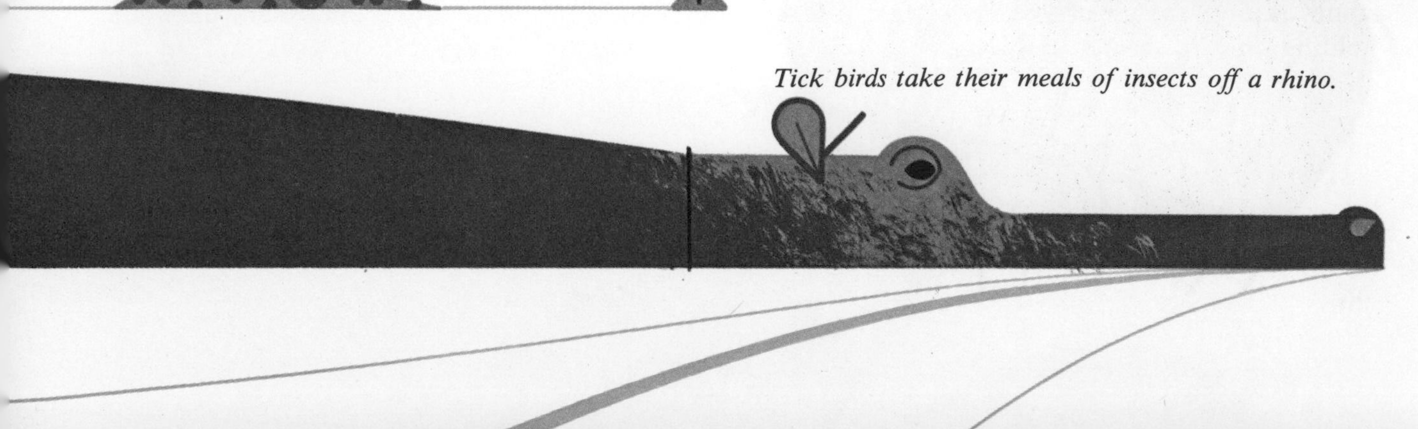

These interlocked antlers tell how two bull moose died in battle.

An okapi washes his ear with his extra long tongue.

the lynx and the bobcat in North America, the ocelot and the jaguarundi of the American tropics. All of these large cats can roar but do not purr. Many kinds of smaller, purring cats are found also throughout the world. The domestic cat, a pet for centuries, maintains a reserve and wildness that add to its fascination.

Several families of flesh-eating mammals are specially fitted for life in the sea but return to land to give birth to their young. These are the walruses, sea lions, and seals. All have streamlined bodies, and their legs are modified as flippers for swimming. On land they waddle clumsily.

The male walrus' ivory tusks may be more than three feet long. The tusks are used for defense, mainly in fights with other males at mating time, and also to dig in mud for clams or other morsels. A walrus' chief enemies are polar bears, killer whales, and man. Eskimos eat their flesh, make homes and boats of their thick hides, and carve the tusks into ornaments.

The true or earless seals are the most completely adapted for life in the sea. Their hind flippers stick out behind like a lobed tail and are almost useless on land. Except in young seals, the fur is coarse and of little value. Most common is the harbor seal. The largest is the bull elephant seal, which may weigh more than two tons and measure 15 feet long. Its grotesque, inflatable snout may be two feet long.

Sea lions, or eared seals, can move about on land with considerable ease. The California sea lion is the common "trained seal" of circuses and marine shows. Most valuable of the sea lions are the fur seals, hunted almost to extinction. A bull may have a harem of as many as a hundred cows, which he herds onto an island and protects from other males until the pups are ready to put out to sea.

Carnivores are the hunters; hoofed mammals are the hunted. They are mostly grazing animals, and many are swift runners. Their eyes, located at the sides of their head, permit them to detect an enemy's approach from almost any direction. In contrast, a hunter's sharp eyes are directed forward.

The horse belongs to the group of hoofed mammals that have an odd number of toes. The horse

A thick-coated alpaca; one of the many animals that have been domesticated by man.

runs on one toe, which ends in a broad, horny hoof. A few wild horses may still live in Mongolia, but the wild horses of the American West were descendants of domestic horses that escaped from early explorers. African zebras are closely related to horses.

Among the other odd-toed hoofed mammals are four species of tapirs, two in South America, one in Central America, and one in southeastern Asia. Rhinoceroses of Africa and Asia also belong to this group. A rhino's hide may be two inches thick, and the animals are too large—weighing up to four tons—to be attacked even by lions. Rhinos are ill-tempered and quick to charge, reaching speeds of more than 30 miles an hour. Both the black and the white rhinos of Africa have two horns; the longest horn of the white rhino may measure three feet in length. The Indian rhino has only one horn.

Pigs are even-toed hoofed mammals. Wild boars are fast, have quick tempers, and can gore with their sharp tusks. Hunting them is a dangerous but popular sport. The apparently useless tusks of the babirussa of southeastern Asia are twisted and curled and may be a foot and a half long. All pigs have long, tough snouts with which the animals root to get their food. They eat mainly fruits, roots, or other plant matter but also kill small animals, including rattlesnakes.

Though its name literally means "river horse," the hippopotamus is a cousin of the pigs. Its eyes and its nostrils are on bumps, enabling the animal to see and breathe while almost completely underwater. Hippos feed on plants growing in and near the water. They can submerge completely and run along the bottom. A large hippo may weigh as much as four tons.

Camels and llamas are closely related animals that live in widely separated parts of the world. Both have been servants of man for centuries. Camels, in fact, are virtually extinct in the wild. The dromedary or one-humped camel once lived in the wild in North Africa. The bactrian or two-humped camel is from South and Central Asia, where a few apparently still roam wild in the Gobi Desert. Camels can travel for days without drinking, utilizing water stored in cells lining their stomach. When water is available, they drink large amounts. The humps are stores of fat that serve as reserve food. With their broad,

A herd of white-bearded gnus watch as two rubbery-necked bull giraffes do battle.

padded feet, camels can move across soft sand without sinking in, and they can carry loads of several hundred pounds. Camels have mean, balky dispositions, and in addition to bucking and kicking, they have the unsavory habit of spitting in the face of the person who has angered them. Desert-dwelling people have long depended on camels to supply them not only with transportation but also with meat, milk, and hides.

Llamas, as cantankerous as camels, live in the grassy plateaus of the Andes in South America. Like camels, they have served people for many years as beasts of burden and as sources of meat, milk, and hides. Alpacas, their smaller relatives, are also domesticated, their long fleece valued in weaving cloth. Guanacos and vicuñas are wild cousins of llamas and alpacas.

Largest of all the hoofed mammals in the Northern Hemisphere is the moose, a member of the deer family. A bull moose weighs nearly 1,500 pounds, and its broad antlers may spread nearly six feet. A big moose has only one really dangerous enemy—man. Moose are now found only in northern wilderness mountain areas. Nearly as large as the moose is the elk, or wapiti, found today only in the wilderness mountain areas of the West. The smaller caribou, or reindeer, lives farther north than any hoofed animal except the musk ox. Herds range the treeless tundra in summer and migrate southward to timbered areas in winter. Caribou use their broad antlers to root up plants and to move away coverings of snow to get food.

The white-tailed deer actually became more abundant in North America as the forests were cut away and grew up in brushland. At the same time its predators were killed off. In the mountains of the West, the mule deer, easily identified by its large, floppy ears, is most abundant. Smallest of the North American deer are the Coue's deer of the Southwest and the Key deer of the Florida Keys. Neither stands much taller than two feet at the shoulders, but both are larger than the tiny brockets of Brazil and the pudus of Chili. In Europe, the fallow, red, and roe are the common deer. Deer shed their antlers every year. Except for the caribou, only the males have antlers.

Most ungainly of the hoofed mammals are giraffes of Africa. They may stand 18 feet tall, with a third of their height consisting of their long neck. Their hind legs are much shorter than their front legs so that the animal slopes sharply from head to tail. Giraffes can easily browse on the tender leaves of tall trees. But to drink or to

A mother elephant disciplines her baby with an uprooted bush.

Killer whale smashes through ice to grab a seal.

feed on ground plants, the animal must spread its front legs wide and bend its head down. The okapi, a short-necked relative of the giraffe, lives in the forests of the Congo.

Most fleet of the hoofed mammals are the antelopes, which belong to the same family as cattle, goats, and sheep. Antelopes are most numerous and most varied in the plains country of Africa and Asia. Some have small, spikelike horns; others, such as the blackbuck of India and the kudu of South Africa, have long corkscrew-shaped horns. These horns are hollow, unlike the solid antlers of deer. Pronghorned antelopes of the American West have hollow, branched horns that are shed. Pronghorns belong to a separate family. All antelopes can run fast. Some kinds, notably the klipspringers and springboks, can leap high.

Biggest of the wild cattle are the water buffalo of India, the Cape buffalo of Africa (one of the most feared of all wild animals), the long-haired yaks of the cold highlands of Tibet, the bison of the North American plains, and the musk oxen of the Arctic. Domestic cattle are descendants of wild cattle of Europe and Africa. The surefooted chamois of the Alps, and wild sheep and goats, including Rocky Mountain goats of North America, the twisted-horned markhors of India, and the sickle-horned ibexes

A bottlenose dolphin plays with a pelican feather.

Tarsiers are big-eyed primitive primates.

Spider monkey gathers food with its prehensile tail.

of Europe, Africa, and Asia also belong to this family. All have hollow horns and chew cuds.

Giants of the present-day land mammals are the elephants, which stand nearly 12 feet tall at the shoulders and may weigh as much as six tons. African elephants are so ponderous that when full-grown they never lie down, even sleeping on their feet—and they may live for more than 40 years. Most remarkable is the elephant's trunk, which is an elongated snout. The elephant sucks water into its trunk and then sprays it into its mouth. With its trunk it reaches high into trees to pull down branches. The trunk is powerful enough to lift logs yet so delicately maneuverable that the elephant can pluck a peanut from the palm of your hand. Of the two kinds—African and Indian—the African elephant is the larger. It has tremendous, floppy ears. Indian elephants, the animals used in circuses and as work animals, have smaller ears.

The largest of all mammals and the largest of animals that have ever lived are blue whales. The blue whale belongs to the group of whales that lack teeth. Instead they have sheets of whalebone, or baleen, at the back of their mouth. Small animals are strained from the water through this sieve. A large whale may eat more than a ton of food a day.

Whales are air breathers, but they may remain submerged for as long as two hours and have been found at depths of nearly a mile. When a whale comes to the surface, it exhales through the blowhole on the top of its head. In cold weather, the hot, moisture laden exhaled air changes quickly into vapor, making a spout. Under the whale's thin, hairless skin is a thick insulating layer of fat, called blubber. Whales do not have a well-developed sense of smell, and their eyes are small but adequate for seeing under the water. Whales give birth to a single young, called a calf, and nurse it under the water. The mother's mammary glands are located in skin-covered pockets at the rear of her body.

Most of the toothed whales, which includes the porpoises, are swift swimmers. The narwhal of arctic waters has only one tooth, which is nearly half the length of its body. The killer whale, which roams all seas, travels in schools and will attack animals of any size, cutting them to shreds. The sperm whale, up to 60 feet long, has an enormous, boxlike head filled with a white oily substance called spermaceti, believed to help cushion the whale against tremendous pressures of the depths in its deep dives. The porpoises are gentle animals and are easily tamed.

Monkeys, apes, and man make up the groups of animals known as primates. As far as intelligence is concerned, they do rate top position. Otherwise, they have few outstanding characteristics. Except for man, the primates are found largely in the tropics, and most are tree dwellers. Most primitive and least manlike are lemurs, tarsiers, and lorises. All are climbers, with big

eyes and thick coats of hair. Most monkeys of the Old World have tails and their nostrils are set close together and open downward. The male proboscis monkey's snout fairly droops over its mouth. Other monkeys of the Old World are the macaques, guerezas, baboons, and mangabeys. The rhesus monkey, a macaque, has been used much in medical research.

Most monkeys of the New World have a long tail that is used as an aid in climbing. Their nostrils are not directed downward. Howlers, spider monkeys, capuchins, and marmosets are among the common kinds of New World monkeys.

Most manlike of the primates are the apes, which live in Asia and Africa. Next to man, they are the most intelligent of all animals. Chimpanzees and gorillas spend most of their time on the ground. They walk on all fours, clenching their fists so their weight rests on their knuckles. Gibbons and orangutans are tree-dwelling apes.

Finally there is man. He ranks himself as supreme among the animals, and by virtue of superior intelligence this cannot be disputed. None of the living primates are his ancestors, though he shares with them a common ancestor. Man is still piecing together the story of his own past. Like other animals, though, he busies himself mostly in finding food and in rearing his young. He differs only in that his brain is the principal tool used in satisfying his needs.

A gibbon catches a weaverbird in midair.

A mandrill in threat position, with teeth bared.

A chimp makes a meal of termites, using a piece of grass as a tool to drag them out of their nest.

With his superior brain and with the use of tools, man dominates the animal kingdom.

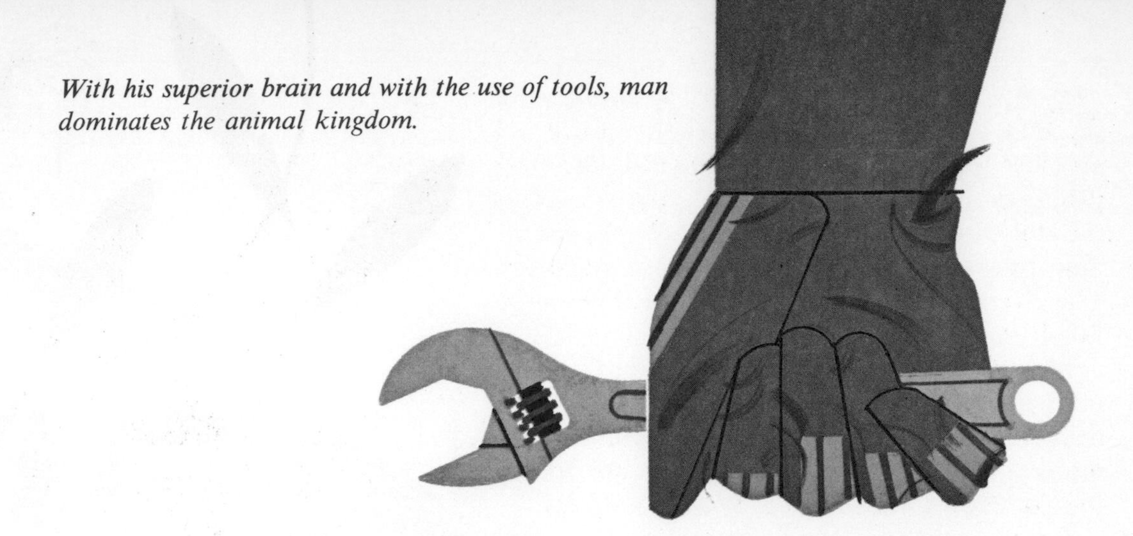

INDEX

Page numbers in **boldface** type refer to illustrations.

Flamingo

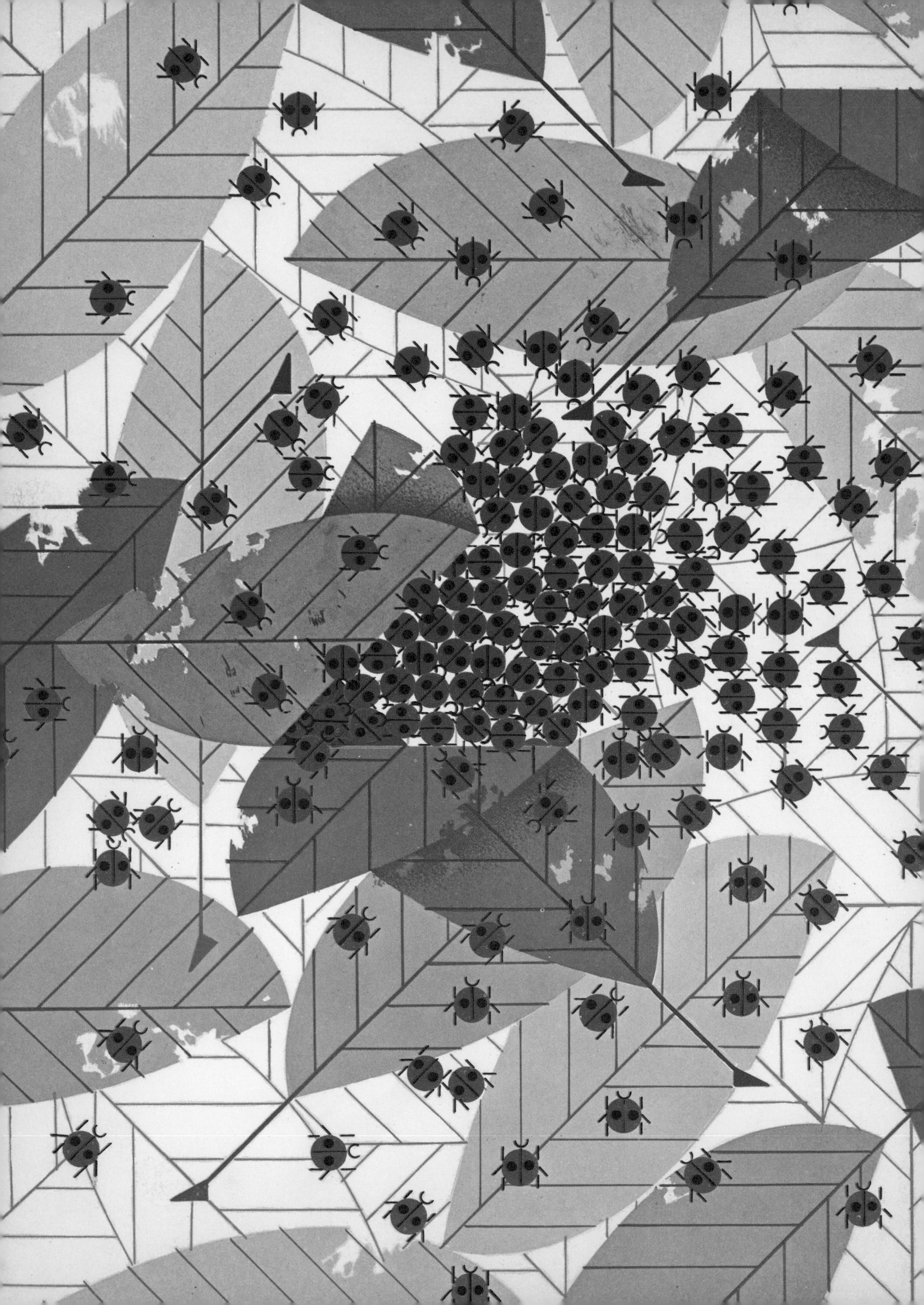